THE BIOLOGY OF
FLOWERS

THE BIOLOGY OF FLOWERS

By

W. O. JAMES AND A. R. CLAPHAM

Department of Botany, Oxford

OXFORD
AT THE CLARENDON PRESS
1935

OXFORD UNIVERSITY PRESS
AMEN HOUSE, E.C. 4
LONDON EDINBURGH GLASGOW
NEW YORK TORONTO MELBOURNE
CAPETOWN BOMBAY CALCUTTA
MADRAS SHANGHAI
HUMPHREY MILFORD
PUBLISHER TO THE UNIVERSITY

PRINTED IN GREAT BRITAIN

PREFACE

In this book flowers are considered as mechanisms securing with varying degrees of success the reproduction of their species, usually by cross-fertilization. Properly speaking this begins with the laying down of the flower's rudiments in the bud and ends only with the production of ripe and viable seeds. Our story includes, therefore, the development of the flower, particularly its essential organs, the conveyance of the pollen from ripe anther to ripe stigma, fertilization of the egg-cell by male gametes from the pollen, and the final development of the seeds. The sequence shows much similarity in essentials throughout the whole range of flowering plants, and it has been possible in the early chapters of this book to describe many of the stages in general terms. Nothing more than this has been attempted for most of the phases of development. When the methods by which pollen is conveyed from one plant to another are considered such a general treatment is much less satisfactory, for even the flowers of very closely allied plants may show entirely different styles of pollination. The table on pp. 110–11 has been compiled to give some idea of the variety of the agencies involved, and also includes the plants we have chosen to represent each class. The examples have been chosen to illustrate the common types of floral mechanism, and no particular regard has been paid to taxonomic status except that several members of the *Ranunculaceae* have been included because this family is so often made an object of special study.

The examination of floral structure with no more elaborate apparatus than a hand-lens has long been recognized as of great educational value, but the methods brought to the task are not always the best. On this account we have ventured in Chapter VI to suggest a system of work that has been found to answer well. The detailed descriptions and drawings in the succeeding chapter are not intended as a substitute for such work, but may serve, we hope, as an encouragement and a guide. Having become acquainted with the methods and some of their results more independent efforts should be possible. The results of an examination are best recorded in two forms, a floral diagram and a drawing of the half flower. The practice of drawing isolated parts torn apart from their essential relations with the rest of the structure is useless and defeats its own ends. It is hard to understand, too, how the idea of limiting the structural drawing to the cut surfaces alone ever arose, and the fact that such an absurdity is still sometimes encouraged is very regrettable. Nothing whatever seems to be gained and most of the essential information may be lost.

Neither of the present authors has had more than the slightest personal

contact with Dr. A. H. Church, lately of this department. It nevertheless remains true that his influence on the preparation of this little book
has been very great, as any one who knows his work will realize. For
various reasons Dr. Church's own writings and drawings are much less
easily available than could be desired and one excuse for the present
volume is that we hope it may help to disseminate the methods he did
so much to improve.

Figs. 5, 6, and 48 are reproduced from Dr. Church's *Types of Floral
Mechanism* and Fig. 71 is based on one of his numerous drawings in
the Oxford Botany Department. Figs. 7 and 8 are redrawn after
Payer (*Traité d'Organogénie Comparée de la Fleur*) and Figs. 3 and 10
are simplifications of Sach's and Hanstein's well-known drawings respectively. Figs. 1 and 2 are reproduced from Strasburger's *Text Book
of Botany*; Fig. 9 from Sladen's *The Humble Bee*, both published by
Macmillan & Co., Ltd. The remainder of the drawings are taken direct
from the plants.

We also wish to acknowledge our indebtedness to Mr. H. Baker for his
help in examining the nectaries of *Caltha*, *Scilla*, and *Primula*.

A. R. C.
W. O. J.

DEPARTMENT OF BOTANY,
    OXFORD
    1935.

CONTENTS

VII. DRAWINGS AND DESCRIPTIONS (*contd.*)

I

THE INFLORESCENCE

FLOWERS are borne in some more or less definite position on the plant. They may be **solitary,** borne singly at the end of a shoot or on a stalk which arises in the axil of an ordinary foliage leaf, or there may be special parts of the plant called **inflorescences,** to which flowers are confined. The inflorescence may end the main plant, or be axillary to a foliage leaf. It may consist of an unbranched axis bearing a number of stalked or unstalked flowers, or it may be more or less richly branched. It usually bears leaves somewhat smaller and simpler in form than those in the vegetative parts of the plant. These are called **bracts.** They are sometimes absent, as in the inflorescence of the Wallflower, *Cheiranthus Cheiri*, and other *Cruciferae*.

There is much variety in the form of inflorescences and their description can be much simplified by the recognition of a few well-defined types. In the simplest of these a growing-point gives rise to an axis bearing bracts, in the axil of each of which a flower is borne. The growing-point may continue to function until it dies, or it may ultimately be used up in the production of a terminal flower. In either case the oldest flowers are near the bottom and the youngest near the top of the axis, and the inflorescence is called **racemose.** If the flowers are stalked, it is a **simple raceme** (Fig. 1 *a*); if unstalked, a **racemose spike.** Sometimes the buds in the axils of the bracts do not give rise to flowers but to lateral branches on which the flowers are borne. These branches may branch again, especially those near the base of the main axis, so that the whole inflorescence becomes conical with the apex uppermost. A branched raceme of this sort is called a **racemose panicle** (Fig. 1 *b*).

In the other main group of inflorescence types, called **cymose,** the axis always terminates in a flower which is the first to open, and branches from the axils of bracts close beneath this terminal flower. The branch terminates in a flower and itself branches in a similar manner, each branch overtopping its parent axis, and bearing a flower younger than that on the parent axis. If each axis has only one lateral branch the cyme is called **monochasial.** Some monochasial cymes have all the branches in one plane: the **scorpioid cyme** with branching alternately to right and to left, and the **helicoid cyme** with all the branches on the same side. Cymes with two branches on each axis are called **dichasial** (Fig. 2). The two often, but not invariably, arise at the same level. **Pleiochasial** cymes have more than two branches on each axis. The effect of the constant overtopping of the parent axes by their

3987   B

branches in dichasia and pleiochasia is to give the inflorescence the form of an inverted cone, in contrast with the erect cone of racemose inflorescences.

Racemose and cymose inflorescences are not absolutely distinct types. Quite often an inflorescence is racemose in its first branching and then cymose in higher orders of branching. A very good example of this is the Horse Chestnut, *Aesculus Hippocastanum.* The branches of the inflorescence are scorpioid cymes, but they are borne in a racemose manner on the main axis, the youngest nearest the top. The branching is stronger at the base, too, as in racemose panicles, not near the apex as in cymose types.

Besides these more generalized inflorescences there are certain highly specialized types which are quite commonly encountered. In the **corymb** the lengths of the flower-stalks are so adjusted that all the flowers are held at the same level. A corymb may be racemose with youngest flowers nearest the centre, or cymose with the oldest flower in the centre. The **umbel** is similar but the flower-stalks all arise at the same point on the main axis. The **compound umbel** is an umbel of umbels and is characteristic of the family *Umbelliferae.* The **capitulum** or **head** has numerous unstalked flowers borne closely packed on a broad receptacle, usually with the oldest flowers outermost and the youngest in the centre. It is the type of inflorescence found in all members of the large family *Compositae*, where the capitula often simulate single flowers by having large marginal flowers which look like petals (Figs. 51, 53, and 57).

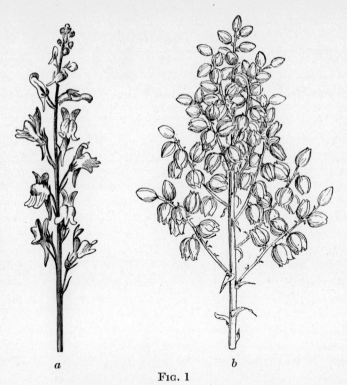

FIG. 1

a. Simple raceme of *Linaria striata* DC.

b. Racemose panicle of *Yucca filamentosa* L.

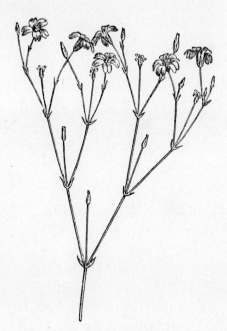

FIG. 2. Dichasial cyme of *Cerastium purpurascens*
Adam. (After Duchartre)

THE FLOWER

Introduction.

THE typical flower consists of an axis whose apical meristem gives rise to four kinds of lateral organs in a definite sequence. The first to be developed are the little leaf-like organs called **bracteoles,** of which there are usually two in Dicotyledons and only one in Monocotyledons. Next are produced the members of the **perianth,** again leaf-like in form, though usually only the oldest members or **sepals,** constituting the **calyx,** are green, the younger members or **petals,** constituting the **corolla,** being brightly coloured. After the perianth has been formed the growing-point gives rise to the **androecium,** whose members are called **stamens,** and finally to the members of the **gynaecium.**

During later development of these organs the axis usually elongates above and below the two bracteoles, and often between them as well, but it fails to elongate appreciably between any other pairs of organs, though it may broaden considerably. The result is that the bracteoles appear separated on a stalk which terminates in a swollen conical **receptacle** bearing very closely packed lateral organs, the lowest and oldest surrounding the uppermost and youngest of these. The name **flower** is usually confined to this terminal cluster of organs.

In some flowers, such as the Buttercup, *Ranunculus*, the organs arise one by one as little bumps beneath the apex with an angle of about 137·5° between successive bumps. That being so, the younger an organ is, the nearer it will be to the apex. A line drawn through successively older organs describes a spiral round the axis, and the organs are said to be **spirally arranged.** In many flowers the members of the corolla, androecium, and gynaecium are in three or more **whorls** or cycles, the members of a whorl arising simultaneously and equally spaced at the same level on the axis. Even in these, however, the bracteoles and sepals usually arise successively, and it seems likely that in many flowers described as whorled all the organs really arise one at a time.

The Bracteoles.

The two bracteoles of Dicotyledons are usually inserted symmetrically to left and right of the flower-stalk, with an angle of about 137·5° between them on the side towards the main axis bearing the flower-stalk. They are the oldest and outermost members of the flower, and may play some part in protecting the growing-point in early stages of development. They often have buds in their axils, and then their position determines the points at which the flower-stalk branches.

In Monocotyledons, where there is only one bracteole, this is on the side towards the main axis. The single bracteole is often very broad and completely encloses the rest of the flower until shortly before opening, protecting it during its upward passage through the soil. It is then called the **spathe,** as in the Snowdrop, *Galanthus nivalis*, Narcissus, Iris, and many other monocotyledonous plants of our gardens.

The Perianth.

The members of the perianth perform two important functions. They constitute the chief protective structures of the developing flower, and are also the means whereby the flower is rendered conspicuous to insects.

Of the flowers described in this book, three, the Marsh Marigold, *Caltha palustris* (Fig. 59), Old Man's Beard, *Clematis vitalba* (Fig. 60), and Bluebell, *Scilla nutans* (Fig. 47), have a perianth consisting of only one kind of member, which therefore carries out both functions. These members are fairly tough in consistency, and are brightly coloured in Marsh Marigold and Bluebell but greenish-white in Old Man's Beard. In most of the other flowers described the perianth consists of two sets of members. The outermost, or **calyx,** is then usually green and is the protective structure completely enclosing the rest of the flower in bud; and the innermost, or **corolla,** is delicate in texture, brightly coloured and often scented, and attracts insects to the flower. There are reasons for believing that the primitive flower was like Marsh Marigold in having only one kind of perianth member, and that the corolla arose later as a set of organs developed in place of some of the outermost stamens, just as additional petals replace some or all of the stamens in double flowers. For this reason the perianth of Marsh Marigold is called a calyx. In the Christmas Rose, *Helleborus niger* (Fig. 40), the curious trumpet-shaped nectary-bearing structures arising within the calyx seem to replace stamens and to be comparable with the petals of Buttercup (which also bear little nectaries near their base), and so are called petals by many writers although they are so different from typical petals.

There are exceptions to the statement that the members of the perianth are the protective and insect-attracting structures of the flower. In some plants the individual flowers are very small and closely packed together in dense inflorescences. When this is so the young inflorescence is usually enveloped by bracts borne at its base, and the sepals are very small, as in Hogweed, *Heracleum Sphondylium* (Fig. 66); completely absent, as in Summer Chrysanthemum, *Chrysanthemum carinatum* (Fig. 53), or replaced by structures which play a part in the dispersal of the fruits, like the pappus hairs in Dandelion, *Taraxacum officinale* (Fig. 57), and the small chaffy scales in *Gaillardia*. Here the petals are still brightly coloured, but in other flowers insects are attracted by brightly coloured bracts or stamens. Thus in both *Thalic-trum aquilegifolium* (Fig. 61) and *Plantago media* the perianth members are quite small and greenish in colour, but the stamens are purple, and it is these which make the flowers conspicuous. Finally, in flowers which are pollinated by wind, not by insects, there is usually no brightly coloured perianth. In Oak, *Quercus Robur* (Fig. 71), the six perianth members are tiny green scales, and in False Oat Grass, *Arrhenatherum elatius* (Fig. 69), the two lodicules, hardly visible with a hand-lens, are believed to represent the perianth.

In many flowers the petals are not separate structures throughout their length, but form a cup or tube at their base. Such corollas are said to be **sympetalous** or **gamopetalous.** They arise when there is meristematic activity beneath the original petal primordia, forming a continuous ring upon which the primordia are raised. The ring, by its further growth, gives rise to the corolla tube, and the original primordia to free lobes which may be quite large, as in Primrose, *Primula vulgaris* (Fig. 44), or hardly apparent as in Bindweed, *Convolvulus.*

Unequal growth of petal primordia gives rise to a flower whose petals are of different sizes, so that the flower is no longer **actinomorphic** or symmetrical about several planes. Usually it is still symmetrical about a plane drawn through the middle of the flower from back to front, as in Sweet Pea, *Lathyrus odoratus* (Figs. 41 and 42), where the left- and right-hand halves of the flower are mirror images. Such flowers are called **zygomorphic.** Occasionally flowers are quite **asymmetrical,** as in Indian Shot, *Canna.*

Sympetaly and zygomorphy of the corolla are combined in Foxglove, *Digitalis purpurea* (Fig. 33), and White Deadnettle, *Lamium album* (Fig. 35).

It will be seen later that sympetaly and zygomorphy play very important parts in facilitating cross-pollination.

The calyx may also exhibit **gamosepaly,** as in White Campion, *Melandrium album* (Fig. 25), zygomorphy, or both, as in Broom, *Sarothamnus scoparius* (Fig. 45).

The Androecium.

The stamens of Flowering Plants are very constant in form and consist of a slender stalk or **filament** broadening at its apex into the **connective** which bears two **anther-lobes,** one each side. Each anther-lobe has a groove running vertically down its outer side, marking the partition wall between two **pollen-sacs.** The whole terminal structure, connective and two anther-lobes, constitutes the **anther.**

The number of stamens varies greatly from flower to flower. Some flowers have very many, either arranged spirally, as in Marsh Marigold, *Caltha palustris* (Fig. 58), or in whorls, as in Raspberry, *Rubus Idaeus*

(Fig. 55). More usually there is a small number, ten or fewer, arranged in one or two whorls, the individual stamens occupying definite positions in relation to the sepals and petals. Thus the five outer stamens of Meadow Cranesbill, *Geranium pratense* (Fig. 38), are opposite the petals, and the five inner stamens opposite the sepals.

In development the stamen arises as a small protuberance on the receptacle, and as it enlarges it gradually assumes the four-lobed form of the mature anther. The filament arises late in development just as the flower is opening, by meristematic activity and elongation of the basal part of the primordium. Each of the four pollen-sacs arises from a single cell beneath the epidermis of the anther-lobe. These **arche-sporial cells** divide repeatedly by ordinary mitotic divisions to form four cell masses which differentiate into central groups of **pollen mother-cells**; layers, one cell thick, surrounding the mother-cells and constituting nutrient layers tapeta (singular **tapetum**); and layers which add to the thickness of the walls of the anther-lobes and play a part in their dehiscence. The pollen mother-cells separate from each other and become rounded. Their nuclei then divide meiotically to form pollen grains arranged in a tetrahedron. The walls of the pollen grains become two-layered, the outer layer growing considerably in thickness. The thickness is not deposited evenly all over the surface, but forms a pattern of spines, grooves, ridges, or plates which is characteristic of the species. Finally this outer wall becomes cutinized and hence highly resistant to chemical and bacterial breakdown, so that pollen grains retaining their characteristic surface-sculpturing may be found in peat deposits several thousands of years old.

When the pollen grains are sculptured and cutinized they are mature, and their liberation from the pollen-sac soon takes place. This is effected by changes in the walls of the anther-lobes resulting ultimately in the breakdown of the partitions separating the two pollen-sacs of each lobe, and the splitting of the outer wall of the lobes along the grooves which originally marked the position of the partitions. A transverse section of an anther shows the mechanism of this splitting or **dehiscence.** The outer wall is three or four cell-layers thick. The outermost layer is a thin-walled epidermis which plays no important part in dehiscence. Beneath this are two or three layers of cells, thickened in a peculiar manner, called **fibrous** or **palisade layers.** Their outer tangential walls are thin, but their inner tangential and radial walls have lignified thickening strips, often branched and interconnected. These cells are found everywhere except along the lateral grooves of the anther. When the pollen is ripe, the wall layers begin to lose water. As the contents diminish in volume the radial walls of the fibrous cells are pulled together, the outer tangential walls being thrown into folds. The cohesion of the cell contents and their adhesion to the wall prevent the

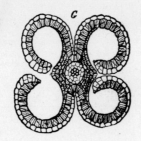

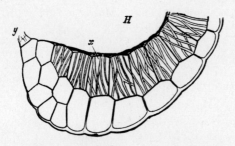

FIG. 3. (Redrawn after Sachs)

G. Transverse section of a dehisced stamen

H. Part of wall more highly magnified

Note the peculiarly thickened cell-layer *x* whose shrinkage brings
about dehiscence at *y* where the cells are all thin-walled

entry of air, and with increasing water-loss the strain on the radial walls becomes progressively greater until, eventually, the unthickened cells along the groove of each anther-lobe are torn apart, and a long gaping slit appears on each side of the anther. The pollen grains are now free to be transported by wind or insects to a receptive stigma.

The Gynaecium.

The gynaecium of Flowering Plants, in contrast with the androecium, is very variable in form, structure, and position. Its morphology is best understood by tracing its probable evolutionary history from those types which are believed on fairly strong evidence to be nearest to the ancestral condition. The Marsh Marigold, *Caltha palustris* (Fig. 59), is the British plant with best claims to primitiveness in the gynaecium. Here the conical receptacle forms, as youngest floral members, about six **carpels.** They arise successively as small protuberances behind the growing-point of the receptacle. They soon assume a horseshoe shape, with the open side uppermost, and the back somewhat elevated. Later meristematic activity occurs at the extreme base of the primordium as well as near the apex. The basal growth gives a hollow, more or less cylindrical structure, the **ovary ;** and the apical growth a short stalk, the **style,** terminating in the **stigma,** covered with sticky papillae. The ovary has a well-marked groove on its inner side, and a section shows that there is an inwardly projecting ridge corresponding with it, and that small almost spherical bodies, the **ovules,** are borne in two rows along the ridge. Down the outer side or back of the ovary is a less conspicuous groove marking the position of a strong vascular bundle. A section across the ovary suggests very strongly that the carpel is a leaf folded upwards, the ovules being borne along the inturned edges, and the dorsal vascular bundle representing the midrib. This must not, however, be taken as literally true, even if it should be demonstrated some day that plants ancestral to Flowering Plants had flattened leaves bearing marginal ovules. Some morphologists call the carpel a leaf, just as they call sepals, petals, and stamens leaves, because its mode of origin and position are comparable with those of a foliage leaf; but it should then be called a tubular or cylindrical leaf, not a folded leaf, to avoid false or dubious implications.

In Buttercup, *Ranunculus* (Fig. 54), also the gynaecium consists of a number of separate carpels, each with basal ovary, short style, and terminal stigma. The ovary differs from that of Marsh Marigold in being smaller and containing only one ovule.

In most flowers the gynaecium is a single structure. Sometimes, as in Annual Larkspur, *Delphinium ajacis*, it is single from the first, there being only one primordium initially. Then it is interpreted as consisting of a single carpel comparable with each carpel of the Marsh Marigold or

Buttercup. More often there are two or more primordia, but the ovary is formed as a single structure by intercalary growth beneath them, so that the primordia come to be seated on the ovary and form only its apex with the styles and stigmas (Fig. 7 *b*). The ovary, containing the ovules, is thus a basal region exactly comparable with the corolla tube of the sympetalous corolla. Ovaries of this type are called **syncarpous** in contrast with **apocarpous** ovaries derived from separate carpels. They are usually surmounted by as many styles (Fig. 25), or by one style with as many stigmas (Figs. 39, 57), as the number of primordia. They may be single chambered—**unilocular**—with ovules borne in rows down the wall (Fig. 48); or many chambered—**multilocular**—with ovules borne on a central column (Fig. 46). The regions of attachment of ovules being called **placentae,** the former arrangement is known as **parietal** and the latter as **axile placentation.** A less frequent arrangement, found in Primrose, *Primula vulgaris* (Figs. 43, 44), is that in which a unilocular ovary has ovules borne on a column rising from the floor but not reaching the roof—**free central placentation.**

Each ovule arises as a small projection from the placenta. It consists of a tissue called the **nucellus** round which one or two envelopes or **integuments** grow up later, completely enclosing it except for a narrow apical pore called the **micropyle.** While the integuments are growing up the nucellus acquires a short stalk and becomes bent through 180° by unequal growth of its two sides until the micropyle points backwards towards the placenta. At a quite early stage a single hypodermal cell of the nucellus enlarges and divides meiotically to form a row of four cells of which only the innermost develops further, the other three becoming crushed and dead. The innermost is called the **embryo-sac.** In its further development it increases its volume considerably, its nucleus giving rise to eight nuclei by three successive mitoses. The eight arrange themselves very characteristically into a micropylar group of three, two **synergidae** and an **ovum;** a central pair, and a basal group of three **antipodal cells.** The synergidae, ovum, and central nuclei acquire sheaths of cytoplasm, but no walls are formed, and they may be regarded as naked cells: the antipodal cells have thin cellulose walls. The two central nuclei later fuse to form what is sometimes called the **secondary nucleus,** sometimes the **polar nucleus.** Stages in this developmental sequence are shown in Fig. 4.

Position of the Ovary.

There is a wide range of variation in the relative positions of the ovary and the other floral members. A frequent and probably primitive condition is that in which a more or less conical receptacle bears apocarpous ovaries as uppermost members or a syncarpous ovary as a terminal structure. The other floral members are then said to be **hypogynous,**

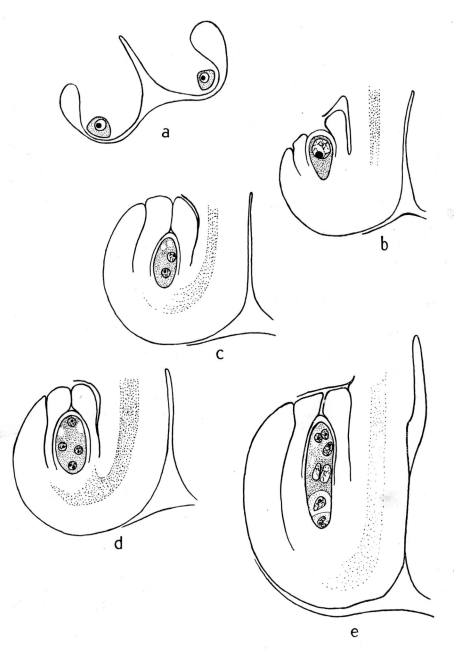

FIG. 4. Stages in development of ovule of *Lilium candidum* L.

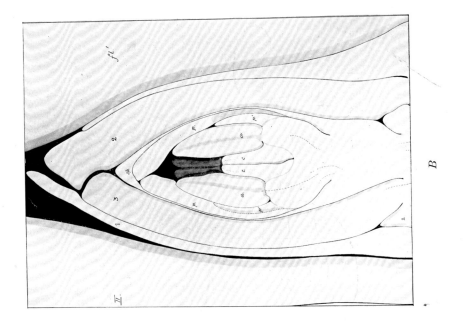

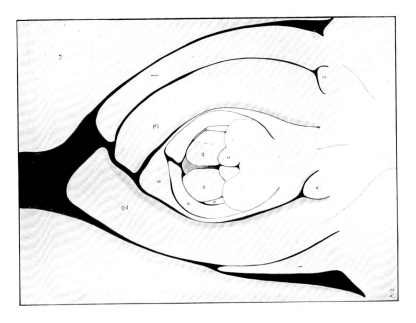

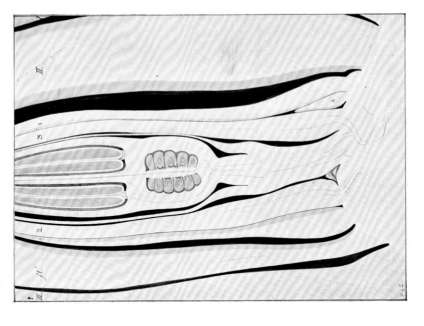

Fig. 5. Stages in development of flower of Snowdrop, *Galanthus nivalis* L. (After Church)

A. Mid July
B. Early August
C. Early September

1, 2, 3, Leaves (with sheathing bases) ;
s, Bracteole ; p, outer, p', inner, perianth segments ; a, anthers ;
c, carpels ; A, end of plant-axis

Note how the carpels fill the receptacular cup from the first, enlarging with it when its concavity is increased by subsequent growth: a simple type of epigyny

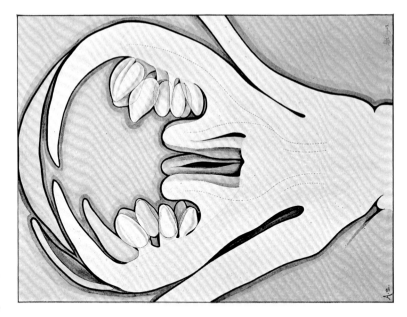

B

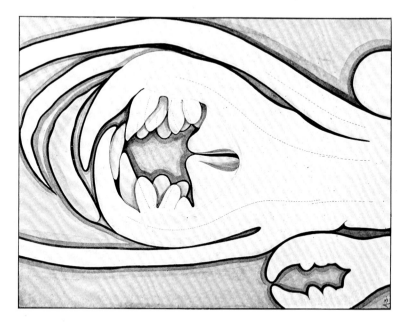

A

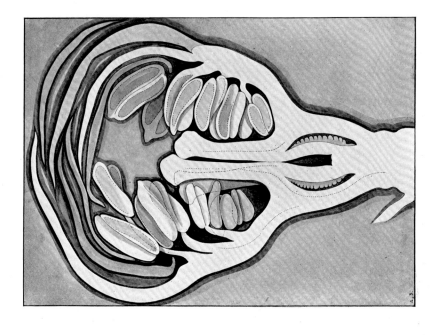

C

FIG. 6. Stages in development of flower of Japanese Quince, *Cydonia japonica* Pers. (After Church)

A, an early stage showing all the floral members arising in the concavity of the cup-shaped receptacle, whose growing-point is at the base of the cup;

B, a later stage, with anthers and carpels differentiating;

C, still later; the stamens, with filaments elongating, are separated from the carpels by a perigynous zone; the carpels have formed styles which are beginning to fuse at their base; the lowest third of the ovary is the result of growth below the growing-point: a complex type of epigyny

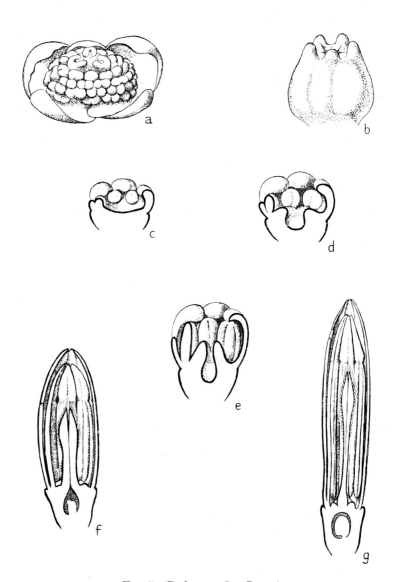

FIG. 7. (Redrawn after Payer)

(*a*) Young flower of *Helleborus foetidus* L., showing spiral arrangement of parts

(*b*) Young syncarpous ovary of *Cerastium Biebersteinii* DC., showing five carpels surmounting the syncarpous region

(*c–g*) Stages in development of flower of *Heliopsis scabra* Dunal. (*Compositae*). Note that the two carpels roof the cavity of the inferior ovary and form the style and stigmas, while the single ovule is borne near the base of the cavity, remote from the carpels

that is, below the ovary; and by an extension of the literal meaning of
the term the whole flower is sometimes called hypogynous. This condition is well seen in Marsh Marigold, *Caltha palustris* (Fig. 59), and
Buttercup, *Ranunculus acris* (Fig. 54), with apocarpous ovaries; and in
the White Campion, *Melandrium album* (Fig. 25), and Foxglove, *Digitalis purpurea* (Fig. 33), with syncarpous ovaries.

There are a few flowers, such as the Violets, *Viola* (Fig. 49), in which
the receptacle is slightly concave, so that the other floral members are
inserted at a somewhat higher level than the ovary. These are usually
called hypogynous, but they grade into the frequent condition known as
perigyny. Here the receptacle is usually concave from the first and
during development there is meristematic activity between the bases
of the stamens and ovaries. Thus a perigynous zone is intercalated in
the receptacular cup, increasing its concavity and separating the other
floral members from the gynaecium.

This perigynous zone shows a wide range of variation in width and
concavity. In some members of the *Rosaceae*, such as Blackberry and
Raspberry, *Rubus* (Fig. 56), Strawberry, *Fragaria*, and Avens, *Geum*, the
flower appears at first sight to be hypogynous, since the receptacle
terminates in a conspicuous cone bearing the numerous carpels. On
closer inspection, however, it is seen that the bases of the stamens are
separated from this cone by a narrow flange, which functions as a
nectary and gives an appearance of slight basal fusion of the calyx,
corolla, and androecium. This flange arises at a fairly late stage in
floral development by meristematic activity of the receptacle beneath
the bases of the stamens, petals, and sepals, and is thus a perigynous
zone.

In Plum and Cherry, *Prunus*, the perigynous zone forms a definite
cup-shaped concavity at the base of which the single carpel is attached.
Here the young ovary may be supposed to be better protected from
desiccation than in hypogynous types, situated as it is in a kind of
'damp chamber'.

Extreme perigyny is seen in the Rose, *Rosa* (Fig. 19), where the very
wide perigynous zone is deeply flask-shaped, the styles protruding
through a narrow apical aperture.

Sometimes associated with perigyny, though often found also in non-
perigynous types, are the conditions known collectively as **epigyny.**
Epigynous flowers are those in which the three outer sets of floral
members—calyx, corolla, and androecium—are borne upon the ovary, or
on a perigynous zone which is itself borne upon the ovary. The ovary
is then termed **inferior,** in contrast with the **superior** ovaries of non-
epigynous types, whether hypogynous or perigynous. They are often
described as flowers in which the ovary is 'fused' with the receptacle,
but this is of course a misleading phrase, since no actual fusions take

place. It seems, in fact, that the epigynous condition may arise in a number of ways. The simplest type, found in Daffodil, *Narcissus*, and Snowdrop, *Galanthus* (Fig. 5), is that in which the receptacle is initially very concave with the carpels attached to it by sloping bases, the other floral members arising near the margin of the cup. During development there is a considerable deepening of the receptacle cup by intercalary growth. The carpels have their areas of attachment much enlarged, the outer 'wall' of the resulting inferior ovary consisting, then, of the extended wall of the receptacular cup. Meanwhile the carpels themselves are growing larger, and ultimately meet laterally, more or less completely filling the inside of the cup. The apical regions of the carpels project above the rim of the cup as styles and stigmas, and surrounding these are the other floral members, seated on the rim of the cup. In types which are perigynous as well as epigynous there is a zone intercalated between the points of insertion of stamens and carpels, the effect of which is to deepen the receptacular cup still more, but the perigynous addition is bare, and does not form part of the ovary.

In other types also called epigynous a zone of growth is situated beneath the growing-point of the receptacle, so that the greater part of the inferior ovary does not, truly speaking, consist of carpels but is a new epigynous zone, the loculi of the carpels being continued as pockets in this new zone, and the actual carpels forming only the apex of the ovary, the style, and the stigmas. This type is seen in Willow-herb, *Epilobium*, Madder, *Rubia*, Bedstraw, *Galium*, Snowberry, *Symphoricarpus* (Fig. 8), and Hogweed, *Heracleum* (Fig. 66). In Quince, *Cydonia* (Fig. 6 *C*), and Apple and Pear, *Pyrus*, both kinds of epigyny are found in the same flower. Figs. 8 *a–f* and 6 *A–C* show how these conditions arise.

A third type of epigyny is seen in *Compositae*, where the two carpels form the style and stigmas and roof a deep receptacular cup with a single ovule at its base. Stages in the development of this type are shown in Figs. 7 *c–g*, and Figs. 51, 53, and 57 show the final condition.

The inferior ovary of the epigynous flower appears to be less protected against desiccation than the superior ovary of an hypogynous or perigynous flower. It is most frequently found, however, where flowers are closely aggregated into dense inflorescences, such as the umbels of *Umbelliferae* and the heads of *Compositae*. The inferior ovaries are packed more or less tightly together and are roofed over by the sepals and petals, so that they are well protected.

Monoecism and Dioecism.

The typical flower has both stamens and carpels and is called **bisexual** or **hermaphrodite** since the sexual cells or gametes are ultimately produced from these structures. There are many plants, however,

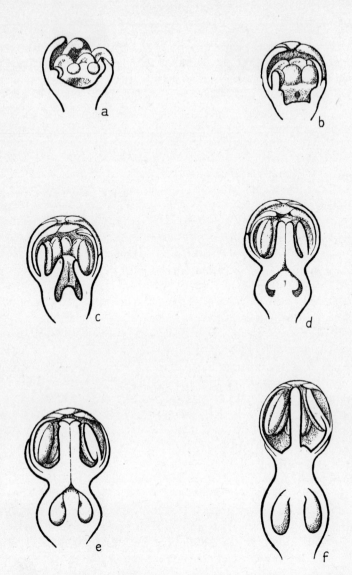

Fig. 8. (Redrawn after Payer.) Stages in the development of the flower
of Snowberry, *Symphoricarpus racemosus* Michx.

The receptacle is concave from the first. The carpels arise on the edge of the cup and form by their fusion the style and stigma. The ovules arise on a central column whose apex is the growing-point of the receptacle. The four septa grow inwards from the wall of the cup and are downward prolongations of the inturned edges of the carpels. An inferior ovary with axile placentation

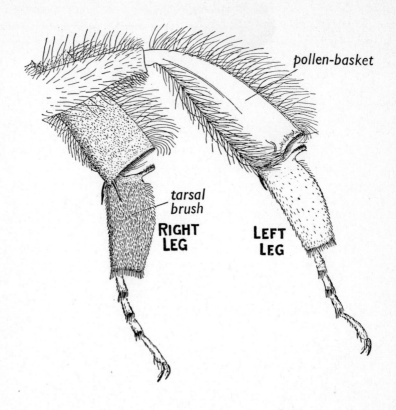

FIG. 9

Pollen collecting apparatus of the queen and worker humble-bee, *Bombus terrestris*

The pollen, after being made into a sticky paste with honey and saliva, is transferred to the tarsal brush, and thence to the pollen-basket on the tibia, the tarsal brush of the right leg filling the basket of the left leg, and vice versa

In the hive bee, *Apis mellifica*, the hairs of the tarsal brush are arranged in transverse rows whose flowers are of two kinds, some having stamens but no carpels and others carpels but no stamens. The former are called staminate and the latter carpellary flowers, and both may be termed unisexual. Sometimes staminate flowers have what appears to be an ovary but is found on closer examination to contain no ovules. This non-functional ovary may act as a nectary, as in White Campion, *Melandrium album* (Fig. 25). Similarly carpellary flowers often bear structures which arise where stamens would be expected and resemble stamens very closely except that no functional pollen is formed in their anthers. Alternatively they may be short teeth or lobes with no anthers. All such sterile structures which replace stamens are called **staminodes**.

If staminate and carpellary flowers are borne on the same individual plant, the species is said to be **monoecious.** Examples are many of our native trees and shrubs such as Oak, *Quercus Robur* (Fig. 71), Beech, Birch, Alder, Hazel. In **dioecious** species staminate and carpellary flowers are borne on different individuals, as in White Campion and Willows. Some species with unisexual flowers have hermaphrodite flowers as well and are then called **polygamous.** Good examples are afforded by the Ash, *Fraxinus excelsior*, where one and the same tree may have staminate, carpellary, and hermaphrodite flowers, and Ground Ivy, *Nepeta Glechoma*, where some plants have hermaphrodite and others carpellary flowers.

III

POLLINATION

Introduction.

POLLINATION consists in the arrival of pollen grains upon the receptive stigma, either of the flower which bore the pollen or of a different flower. The former is called self- and the latter cross-pollination. If pollination does not take place, the ovules shrivel and die and the flower fails to perform its function of reproducing the species.

It has doubtless been realized for many thousands of years that transference of pollen from the staminate to the carpellary flowers is essential for the formation of dates, figs, and a few other cultivated fruits. The early hybridizers effected artificial pollination of a large number of flowers, but Joseph Gottlieb Kölreuter (1733–1806) was the first to draw attention to the ways in which flowers are pollinated naturally. By the close of last century an enormous mass of material had been collected and collated, but, despite an active and long-maintained interest in the subject, there are still many unsolved problems. Light may at length be thrown on them as our knowledge of cytology and genetics increases.

Insect Pollination.

The great majority of flowers are visited by insects which carry pollen grains from dehisced anthers to receptive stigmas. Such flowers are said to be insect pollinated or entomophilous.

TYPES OF INSECT VISITORS.

The insects which visit flowers do not effect pollination consciously or deliberately. Their visits are undertaken in search of food, and pollination takes place quite incidentally. Flowers offer two main kinds of food—pollen and the sugary solution known as nectar. Nectar is not invariably present, or may be present when there is no pollen, as in a carpellary flower or one in which the stamens mature very late.

By far the most important visitors to flowers are the Bees, *Apidae*, belonging to the class *Hymenoptera*. Bees feed on pollen and nectar both when young and adult, and they display a number of adaptations for securing these foods. The most important of these are pollen-collecting hairs on legs or abdomen, and mouth-parts modified for sucking nectar. The collecting hairs of the Hive-bee, *Apis mellifica*, Humble-bees, *Bombus*, and others are on the lower half of the hind-legs (Fig. 9). There are stiff downwardly directed hairs, often with feathery branches, on the basal joint of the tarsus. These constitute the 'tarsal brush' with which the bee collects the pollen. On the tibia there are longer hairs forming baskets for carrying pollen which is placed in them with the tarsal brushes. In the most highly specialized types of bees such as Hive-bees and Humble-bees the pollen is moistened with a little ejected honey before being collected by the tarsal brushes. By this means the pollen masses are made more coherent and can be heaped high above the hairs which form the sides of the carrying basket. Bees with abdominal collecting hairs include the species of *Anthidium* and *Megachite*. In these almost the whole of the lower surface of the abdomen is covered with stiff backwardly directed bristles with which pollen is both collected and carried. Occasionally pollen may be scraped from other parts of the body by means of the tarsal brushes and then transferred to the abdominal brush, but much more frequently it is swept up directly by the abdominal brush. The amount of pollen which a bee can carry is quite large. The Hive-bee is said to carry on each hind leg a pollen mass measuring on the average 3·5 mm. in length by 2 mm. in breadth, and some bees have been observed with loads half their own weight, containing several hundreds of thousands of pollen grains.

The mouth-parts of nectar-sucking bees are considerably modified as compared with their carnivorous ancestors. The important feature is that the bee can place certain organs so as to form a long tube up which the nectar is drawn by the action of a special sucking stomach. When not in use the components of the tube can be folded and withdrawn into a cavity behind the mandibles. While the sucking organs, or proboscis as they are conveniently termed, are in this position, the mandibles are free for use in biting or in loosening pollen from dehisced anthers.

The length of the extended proboscis varies greatly in different kinds of bees, and since this determines whether the nectar in a given flower will or will not be accessible, it is a matter of considerable importance to the study of pollination. The table shows the lengths for a number of the commonest flower-visiting bees.

Prosopis spp.	. . . .	1–1·25 mm.
Halictus spp.	. . . .	1·5–6 mm.
Apis mellifica	. . . .	6 mm.
Anthophora pilipes	. . .	19–21 mm.

	Workers	*Queens*
Bombus terrestris . .	8–9 mm.	9–11 mm.
Bombus lapidarius . .	10–12 mm.	12–14 mm.
Bombus hortorum . .	14–16 mm.	19–21 mm.

It will be seen that the Hive-bee, *Apis mellifica*, has a rather short proboscis, exceeded by all the common species of Humble-bee, *Bombus*; and that the early spring bee, *Anthophora pilipes*, and the queens of *Bombus hortorum* have the longest proboscises, about four-fifths of an inch in length. Although the Hive-bee is debarred from visiting flowers in which the nectar is more than 6 mm. from the nearest point that its head can reach, yet its large demands for pollen and nectar with which to feed its larvae, its long period of activity, its highly developed sense-organs, and its capacity to learn to reach nectar by a complicated route make it by far the most important of all pollinating insects, visiting a wider range of flowers than any other species. The Humble-bees besides having long proboscises are the heaviest and strongest bees, and this enables them alone to enter certain flowers with tightly closed corollas, such as Snapdragon, *Antirrhinum*.

Next most important as flower visitors are the *Lepidoptera*, Butter-flies and Moths, in which the adults feed exclusively on nectar. They differ from bees in that they never take pollen deliberately, and do not feed their larvae on flower foods. They nevertheless visit a wide range of flowers and there are many in which the nectar is accessible only to them. This is because the mouth-parts of *Lepidoptera* are modified into a sucking proboscis which may be of very considerable length, far longer than the longest proboscises of bees. When not actually in use the proboscis is coiled into a tight spiral. The table gives the lengths of the proboscises of some common British *Lepidoptera*, and of a Brazilian hawkmoth, *Macrosilia Cluentius*, described by Fritz Müller.

Smerinthus tiliae (Lime Hawkmoth) . . .	3 mm.
Vanessa urticae (Small Tortoiseshell) . . .	14–15 mm.
Pieris brassicae (Cabbage White)	16 mm.
Macroglossa stellatarum (Humming-bird Hawkmoth)	25–28 mm.
Sphinx ligustri (Privet Hawkmoth) . . .	37–42 mm.
Sphinx convolvuli (Convolvulus Hawkmoth) . .	65–80 mm.
Macrosilia Cluentius	250 mm.

Butterflies usually fly during the daytime, but most moths fly at dusk or during the night, and are the chief visitors to flowers open only at night, such as Tobacco Plants, *Nicotiana*, and Night-Scented Stock, *Matthiola*. The Hawkmoths are the most active Lepidopteran flower visitors. A few, like *Macroglossa stellatarum* fly by day, but most fly by night. They are recognizable by their extremely swift flight and by the fact that they do not alight on flowers but hover in front of them while taking nectar. A day-flying hawkmoth has been observed to visit two hundred violets, *Viola calcarata*, in seven minutes.

Many flies, *Diptera*, are also flower visitors, taking both pollen and nectar. By far the most important flies in transferring pollen are the Hover-flies, *Syrphidae*, recognizable by their alternate hovering and darting flight. They have proboscises of which one part serves to extract pollen and rub it into separate grains before passing it back to be swallowed, while other parts can be pressed together to form a tube for sucking nectar. Some hover-flies have quite long proboscises, so that they vie with humble-bees and butterflies in reaching nectar from the base of a deep corolla-tube. There is, however, a considerable range in length:

Syrphus	2–4 mm.
Eristalis	4–8 mm.
Volucella bombylans . . .	8 mm.
Rhingia rostrata . . .	11–12 mm.

The Bee-flies, *Bombylius*, with a strong superficial resemblance to bees, take nectar only, never feeding on pollen. Their proboscises are 10–12 mm. long.

Besides the highly specialized flies there are hundreds of species with short proboscises which obtain some or all of their food from flowers and which play a large part in the pollination of flowers with easily accessible nectar.

Much less important as pollinators are wasps, of which some feed on flower-food alone while many feed also on fruit juices and on other insects. Some beetles also show modifications for taking nectar, and many eat pollen. Members of other classes of insects, such as grasshoppers and bugs, are sometimes found in flowers and must occasionally transfer pollen, but they do not merit special attention here.

NECTAR AND NECTARIES.

The insects which visit flowers obtain part or all of their food from them. This food may be pollen or nectar or both. Pollen, as has been seen, consists of tiny grains formed in the anthers and liberated by their dehiscence. It is nutritious by virtue of the proteins and fats in each grain. Nectar is a solution of sugars, especially cane-sugar, glucose, and some fructose, the relative proportions and total concentration being very variable. Small quantities of nitrogenous substances, such as albumins, are sometimes present also.

Nectar arises from a special tissue or from hairs in localized areas known as nectaries. These areas vary in position from flower to flower. The most frequent type of nectary is an entire or interrupted ring round the base of the ovary, as in White Deadnettle, *Lamium album* (Fig. 35). In perigynous flowers the perigynous zone often functions as a nectary, as in Raspberry, *Rubus Idaeus* (Fig. 56); and in epigynous flowers the secreting ring lies on the top of the inferior ovary, within the bases of the stamens, as in Hogweed, *Heracleum Sphondylium* (Fig. 66). In Buttercup, *Ranunculus* (Fig. 54), the nectaries are borne one on the base of each petal, covered with a flap so that nectar collects in the little pockets so formed. The petals of Columbine, *Aquilegia* (Fig. 29), and two of the petals in Larkspur, *Delphinium* (Fig. 31), and Monkshood, *Aconitum* (Fig. 27), also carry nectaries, but in all three a part of each nectary-bearing petal forms a spur. The nectary is within the spur, where the nectar is retained after secretion. The trumpet-shaped nectaries of Christmas Rose, *Helleborus niger* (Fig. 40), are somewhat familiar, but smaller and more numerous. In Old Man's Beard, *Clematis Vitalba* (Fig. 60), there is a slight secretion of nectar from the filaments of the outermost stamens, and in Marsh Marigold, *Caltha palustris* (Fig. 59), there is a secretion from hairs at the sides of the carpels but often no nectar can be seen. Many Monocotyledonous flowers, such as Bluebell, secrete from nectaries in the partition-walls of their multi-locular ovaries, the so-called septal glands. Violets, *Viola* (Fig. 49), are unusual in having nectar-secreting tails hanging from the bases of the two front stamens, the nectar collecting in the spur of the front petal.

In most flowers the nectar is retained after secretion in the cup formed by the bases of the petals. Sympetalous flowers, some of which have very long corolla-tubes, are evidently better fitted for holding nectar than flowers with petals free to the base. A few flowers, as already mentioned, have special nectar-holding sacs or spurs.

Some flowers which have no obvious nectaries have patches of specialized cells, thin-walled and filled with a sugary sap. These are usually on the bases of the petals, and can be punctured readily by bees and by some butterflies which then feed upon the sap. Examples are afforded by the British species of *Orchis*, where cells of this type line the inside of the spur.

Finally, there are many flowers which offer only pollen to the visiting insect. Examples are Broom, *Sarothamnus scoparius* (Fig. 45) and lesser Plantain, *Plantago media*.

THE COLOUR AND SCENT OF FLOWERS.

The most striking characteristic of the typical flower is that it is brightly coloured, making it conspicuous from a distance. Since flowers which are not visited by insects are rarely brightly coloured, it seems an easy inference that the bright colours make the flowers conspicuous to insects as well as to us. This has been disputed by many biologists, who claim that insects are attracted to the flowers either by their characteristic scents or by the smell of nectar. The result of much patient research, however, is to give good grounds for believing that many insects have a colour vision much like our own, or at any rate much like that of partially colour-blind persons.

Recent experiments on the hive-bee and on the hawkmoth, *Macroglossa stellatarum*, are those that have led to the least equivocal inferences. It was shown conclusively that hive-bees could distinguish blue and yellow from each other and from all shades of grey. Hence bees really see blue and yellow in some such way as we see them, whereas red is not seen as a distinctive colour. Other workers have confirmed this, showing that bees fly directly from a distance of about 50 cm. towards artificial flowers whose colours have a blue or yellow component, but are not similarly attracted by red. The day-flying hawkmoth, *Macroglossa stellatarum*, the hover-fly, *Volucella*, and the bee-fly, *Bombylius*, gave practically similar results.

Even before these facts had been established it had been claimed by many observers that there is a relation between the colours of flowers and their most frequent visitors. The table on pp. 110–11 gives some idea of the evidence for this view. Sections 2 and 3 include thirteen flowers visited almost exclusively by bees. Nine of these are some shade of purple, two yellow, and two white. These proportions would not have been much changed if the numbers had been larger. Flowers visited chiefly by bees are usually blue-purple, orange, yellow, or sometimes white. They are rarely pure red. These facts become intelligible when it is known that bees see blue and yellow but cannot see red as a distinctive colour, and that they therefore see purples as blue. Similarly an orange flower would appear yellow, its red component contributing nothing to its conspicuousness. White flowers reflect a great deal of light and are seen as conspicuous objects in contrast with the less brightly reflecting background. This would explain why most flowers pollinated by night-flying moths are white, or nearly white, like Honeysuckle, *Lonicera periclymenum* (Fig. 23), and White Campion, *Melandrium album* (Fig. 25). Flowers pollinated by butterflies, on the other hand, are often red. Examples are Maiden Pink, *Dianthus deltoides*, and Red Campion, *Melandrium rubrum*. Butterflies, nevertheless, frequently visit flowers of other colours, yellow, purple, or blue. Beetles and small flies have no evident colour preferences, and are often seen on dull yellow or whitish flowers. The flowers pollinated by carrion-flies are generally dull red or red-brown.

There are many exceptions to these generalizations, and it is evident that insects must often be led to visit flowers for other reasons than their distinctive coloration. Even for insects which are completely colour-blind flowers must often be conspicuous because they reflect more light than their background, appearing therefore as bright patches. But many quite small and inconspicuous flowers are visited so freely that it can only be concluded that they appeal to other senses than vision. This is confirmed by the fact that insects continue to visit, though less frequently, certain flowers such as Foxglove, *Digitalis purpurea*, whose corollas have been cut almost completely away. Such experiments are usually interpreted as showing that insects are attracted by the scent of flowers or by the smell of nectar.

Kerner once marked a Convolvulus Hawkmoth, *Sphinx convolvuli*, and placed it a hundred yards from a plant of honeysuckle. At twilight the moth, previously stationary, stretched its wings and flew straight to the Honeysuckle, where Kerner found it sucking nectar from the flowers. There is no doubt that the moth had detected the perfume of the Honeysuckle from a hundred yards away. Most other flowers visited by night-flying moths are like Honeysuckle in having a heavy scent, and the moths seem first to be attracted by this, and only when they approach more closely are they guided by actually seeing the white corollas. How far this is true of any day-flying insects, however, it is not easy to say. Experiments on hive-bees and humble-bees show conclusively that these insects have a sense of smell not very different from ours. They can be trained to distinguish scents which we can distinguish, but confuse scents which seem similar to us. They can rarely detect scent from a greater distance than we can, and there is little doubt that scent plays only a minor part in attraction from afar. Thus, hive-bees trained to associate the scent of clove-oil with sugar-solution would fly equally frequently and directly towards blue artificial flowers with or without scent, and only on close approach would they swerve away from the scentless flower. Similarly humble-bees, trained with clove-oil, flew much more frequently to blue flowers without the scent than to red, orange, or green flowers with the scent.

When the insects are close to the flower, having been attracted from a distance usually by colour but sometimes by scent, they may be led actually to explore for nectar or pollen by a characteristic scent or form or by the so-called honey-guides. Again it is not easy to disentangle the roles of smell and vision, but it seems that both are involved in this final stage of attraction. A bee will turn from one flower to another of similar colour if the former does not and the latter does emit a scent which it has learnt to associate with food. Experiments with artificial flowers show that this may be due to scent alone, but under natural conditions differently scented flowers of the same colour are usually different also in form, and hive-bees and day-flying hawkmoths can learn to distinguish certain simple patterns in a single colour, provided they resemble the plans of open corollas. Thus a many-rayed star can be distinguished from a four-armed cross. They can also distinguish certain colour patterns, for example a yellow circle in a blue ring from a blue circle in a yellow ring. Now many flowers have an 'eye' differently coloured from the rest of the corolla. Many, too, have lines on their petals, different in colour from the background, radiating out from the centre of the flower. These eyes and lines are called honey-guides. An analysis of the colour combinations in large numbers of flowers has shown that there is almost invariably a real colour contrast for the insect which can probably learn to recognize the colour pattern so presented and thus be aided in selecting the appropriate flowers from amongst many of the same general colour. The name 'honey-guides' is unfortunate, since they are found in some flowers which do not secrete nectar, such as Lupin, *Lupinus polyphyllus* (Fig. 37), and Broom, *Sarothamnus scoparius* (Fig. 45).

As a summary of the last two sections it can be said that many insects habitually visit flowers for the sake of the food which they find in them. Young insects fly towards conspicuous patches of colour or pleasing smells. They thus frequently come upon nectar or pollen. After a time they learn to associate certain colours, forms, and scents with a copious and easily accessible food-supply, so that older insects can pick out appropriate flowers very rapidly. This is especially true of bees, hawk-moths, and certain high-grade flies such as hover-flies and bee-flies; butterflies, beetles, and small flies seem to learn much less rapidly and effectively.

THE MECHANISM OF POLLINATION.

When an insect sucks nectar or takes pollen from a flower whose anthers have dehisced it will often carry some pollen away with it, adhering to its body, head, legs, or proboscis. If it should visit another flower of the same species, some of this pollen may adhere to the stigma and cross-pollination will have been effected. It is now known that this is the way in which pollination usually takes place in a very large number of flowers, and in the second half of this book a small representative set of these flowers is described.

Most flower-visiting insects have hairs on some parts of their body. Thus humble-bees and hive-bees are hairy all over, and though some of them remove pollen from their bodies with their tarsal brushes, this operation can never be complete. Most *Lepidoptera* have hairy heads and most flies hairy legs. Pollen may also be carried on the sticky proboscises of bees, *Lepidoptera*, and flies, on the wings of flies and on the underside of the body of small flies and beetles. Some tiny insects, indeed, may be dusted all over with pollen which adheres everywhere but on highly polished chitinous surfaces.

It is generally found that the insects which visit a flower habitually are those whose size and shape are such that the anthers and stigmas come inevitably into contact with a part of the insect to which pollen can adhere. They are also the insects whose size and shape are such that nectar, if present, is easily accessible. For examples Section 2 of the table on pp. 110–11 may again be consulted. The six flowers listed are all visited by humble-bees. Five of them are a shade of purple which the bee sees as the distinctive colour blue; the other has white flowers crowded in inflorescences. Four of them have nectar in long corolla-tubes or spurs, accessible only to a long-tongued insect; Lupin, *Lupinus polyphyllus* (Fig. 37), which has no nectar, is so constructed that only an insect as heavy as a humble-bee can reach the pollen; and in the Foxglove, *Digitalis purpurea* (Fig. 33), a smaller and shorter-tongued insect than a humble-bee can reach nectar only by crawling some distance into the long corolla-tube. In all, the stamens and stigmas are so placed that a humble-bee must touch them with its back, belly, or head at some stage during a successful visit, so that in passing from flower to flower pollen is carried from the anthers of one to the stigmas of another and cross-pollination is thus effected. These humble-bee flowers have a further feature in common: there is always a landing-stage, so that the insect can alight and get a secure foothold before exploring for food. This is generally formed by one or more perianth segments, sepals, or petals, at the front of the flower, which consequently become zygomorphic. Only in Columbine, *Aquilegia vulgaris* (Fig. 29), is the flower actino-morphic.

Honeysuckle, *Lonicera periclymenum* (Fig. 23), pollinated by hawk-moths, affords an interestingly different type. The flower is whitish in colour and heavily scented, facilitating its recognition by night-flying moths. Moths have extremely long proboscises, and the nectar in Honey-suckle is at the base of a tube 20–25 mm. long. Moths do not alight when sucking nectar, and the flower of Honeysuckle has no landing-stage. Its anthers and stigma are held well outside the corolla-tube, so that the moth touches them with its hairy head or body while hovering before the flower.

Besides these special relations to the most frequent insect visitors the six flowers considered all show another important feature: their anthers and stigmas mature at different times, the anthers before the stigmas. While the anthers are dehiscing they are so held that the insect touches them and removes pollen. Later, when the anthers have almost withered, the stigmas are mature and they are moved in their turn so that they can be touched by the part of the insect to which pollen adheres. It is evident that through this separation in time of maturity, or **dichogamy,** insects must usually bring about cross- rather than self-pollination. There are two kinds of dichogamy: **protandry,** in which anthers mature before stigmas, and **protogyny,** which is the reverse of this. Protandry is the more frequent but both are very widespread. Sometimes dichogamy is very pronounced, as in Hogweed, *Heracleum Sphondylium* (Fig. 66), where the stamens fall before the stigmas mature, but more often there is a period during which both anthers and stigmas are mature, so that the probability of self-pollination is not excluded.

Some insect-visited flowers, like the Sweet Violet, *Viola odorata* (Fig. 49), are not dichogamous, but the relative positions of anthers and stigmas make self-pollination practically impossible. Others, like White Campion, *Melandrium album* (Fig. 25), have staminate and carpellary flowers on different plants, so that self-pollination is completely excluded.

The flowers referred to in the last few paragraphs are all rather highly specialized. The insect visitors have to stand in a definite position and thrust long proboscises in a definite direction. Only high-grade insects, bees, hawkmoths, and a few flies, can acquire the habit of performing such complicated actions with rapidity and precision. There are very large numbers of flowers, however, in which the relation of colour and form of the flower to the visiting insects and the mechanisms which favour cross-pollination are much less evident. Nectar or pollen, or both, are freely exposed to any insect visitor, and dichogamy is slight or absent. There are very few, however, in which self-pollination is the rule. Often cross-pollination is very likely to take place if insects come, but there is a period during which self-pollen may reach the stigma either with or without help from insects. Examples are Buttercup, *Ranunculus acris* (Fig. 54), and Raspberry, *Rubus Idaeus* (Fig. 56).

CONSTANCY OF INSECTS.

Generally speaking only pollen from another flower of the same species is effective on the stigma. If foreign pollen arrives, it either fails to germinate or the pollen-tubes shrivel at an early stage of development. Effective cross-pollination can only take place if an insect visits two flowers of the same species within a fairly short period. It is a matter of interest, then, to discover how far insects confine their attention to a single type of flower or to a restricted number of types. There are two ways of investigating the problem. Individual insects may be watched as they pass from flower to flower, or the pollen grains carried by an insect may be identified by microscopic examination. Both methods have been used on many occasions, and it has been found that bees, hawkmoths, and high-grade flies show a fairly high constancy in the flowers visited during a single journey. As an example, Clements analysed the pollen-loads of 207 bees, of which 121 carried pure loads, 67 pollen of two species, and only 19 of more than two species. The hive-bee shows the greatest constancy, while butterflies and small flies show very little.

Besides increasing the chances of cross-pollination, constancy is probably advantageous to the insect in that it leads to ready recognition and rapid exploitation of the selected flower. It will learn to know how to stand in the best position on the flower, and how far and in what direction to insert its proboscis. It is interesting in this connexion that bees in a mixed garden will fly from flower to flower of the same species even when it is represented by many different colour strains, and will ignore all the other species present. This must be due to a capacity to recognize its characteristic form and scent at close quarters, apart from its colour.

It is evident that constancy can only be absolute at the height of the flowering season of a fairly common plant. Insects cannot visit exclusively flowers which are sparsely scattered, or they would take too long to satisfy their wants. For the same reason they cannot continue to be constant until the very end of the flowering season of a common plant, but there must be a period during which they are dividing their attentions between this and a plant whose flowers are just beginning to appear. The chance that a plant will be cross-pollinated must, in fact, be much increased with an increase in the number of similar flowers in the neighbourhood.

ILLEGITIMATE VISITS.

Flowers are sometimes visited by insects which can take pollen or nectar without effecting cross-pollination. The Foxglove, *Digitalis purpurea* (Fig. 33), for example, has nectar at the base of a long but wide corolla-tube, and small flies and beetles can crawl into the flower and reach it without touching the anthers and stigmas. More usually flowers with nectar at the base of a long tube are protected from this kind of 'illegitimate' visitor by the narrowness of the tube, by a ring of scales or hairs which permit the passage of a proboscis but not of a crawling insect, or by the actual closing of the entrance to the tube so that only strong and heavy insects can force their way in. Examples are Primrose, *Primula vulgaris* (Fig. 44), with a very slender tube, White Deadnettle, *Lamium album* (Fig. 35), with a guard-ring of hairs, and Snapdragon, *Antirrhinum majus*, with a closed entrance. Even these protections do not completely exclude useless visitors. The large but short-tongued humble-bee, *Bombus terrestris*, is much addicted to biting holes through the corolla-tubes of all three and of many similar flowers at a level which enables it to reach nectar from the side. In 'stealing' nectar in this way it evidently cannot bring about cross-pollination, and tends to deter legitimate visitors from continuing to make unprofitable searches for food. Hive-bees may do the same, or may use holes already made by a humble-bee.

Wind Pollination.

A familiar sight in the early months of the year is the cloud of pollen which rises from a hazel bush when a breeze sways the staminate catkins. It is composed of countless numbers of small light pollen grains which do not stick together like those of insect-pollinated flowers and which can therefore be blown easily in the wind. The total quantity of pollen is enormous, and there is a high chance that some of it will reach the projecting stigmas of the carpellary flowers and thus bring about anemophily or pollination by wind, not by insects.

Many other Flowering Plants are like Hazel in being wind-pollinated and have many features in common with it. Amongst them are most of our common native British trees, including Oak, Beech, Birch, Alder,

Elm, and Ash, and all our grasses, sedges, and rushes. There are also several isolated species closely related to insect-pollinated types. The examples described in this book are listed in the table on pp. 110–11. The most obvious characteristic of all these plants is that their flowers are very inconspicuous, usually green in colour and individually small, though they are often grouped in dense inflorescences. Their corollas are not brightly coloured but either consist of greenish scales or are completely missing. There is no scent and no nectar. Their stamens usually have long filaments which are very slender, and, since they are not enclosed within a large corolla, they are easily swayed by the wind. The anthers are often long and slender, and often, too, are attached near the middle so that they can rock about the point of attachment. The pollen is light and powdery and is produced in large quantities. The stigmas are large, usually much branched, and project from the flower so that pollen can easily be caught on them. Self-pollination is quite excluded in most of our wind-pollinated trees and sedges by the fact that the flowers are unisexual. In rushes it is made less probable than cross-pollination by strong protogyny, and in grasses by the suspension of the anthers well below the stigmas at the ends of the very long filaments.

Insects do not often visit these wind-pollinated flowers, which are conspicuous neither by colour nor perfume. If they happen to alight on a flower with mature anthers they may collect some pollen, but this is usually difficult through the absence of an adequate landing-stage and the length and flexibility of the filaments, and because the pollen grains do not stick together into masses which can easily be carried. There is no nectar, and the insect is very unlikely to acquire the difficult and unprofitable habit of making regular visits to such flowers. There is still less inducement to visit the carpellary flowers of plants with unisexual flowers, since there is not even pollen to be obtained from them, so that cross-pollination by insects can take place only very rarely and accidentally.

There are some few plants whose flowers are pollinated sometimes by wind and sometimes by insects. They usually have no nectar and combine certain of the characteristics of typical wind-pollinated and typical insect-pollinated types. Examples in this book are Lesser Meadow Rue, *Thalictrum minus* (Fig. 62), and Lesser Plantain, *Plantago media* (p. 105).

Bird Pollination.

Many tropical and sub-tropical flowers are pollinated not by insects but by birds. Ornithophilous flowers are usually large, secreting nectar in abundance. They are brightly coloured, usually red, and have projecting stamens and styles which are very thick and stiff. The pollinating birds are humming-birds and honey-suckers which hover in front of the flower while they suck nectar with their long beaks. They are often very small, little larger than moths, and they effect cross-pollination by touching the anthers and stigmas of the flowers with their breasts, just as moths do. The stiffness of the filaments and styles is presumably related to the weight and strength of the birds which would otherwise cause serious damage. Investigations on the colour sense of the birds show that they can distinguish red and green as distinctive colours, but not blue. This is in line with the predominance of bright reds in ornithophilous flowers.

Ornithophily is by no means rare. Porsch has estimated that 18 per cent. of the genera of the Brazilian flora have ornithophilous species, and the figures may be little lower in Madagascar, West Australia, and elsewhere. The large-flowered species of *Fuchsia*, natives of South America but often grown in greenhouses, are the most familiar examples to be seen in this country.

Other Pollinating Agents.

A small number of flowers are hydrophilous, pollinated through the agency of water. Thus the Canadian Pondweed, *Elodea canadensis*, is dioecious, and both staminate and carpellary flowers are at first submerged. When mature the staminate flowers are detached and rise to the surface where they open and scatter abundant pollen on the water. In floating it may come into contact with stigmas of a carpellary flower raised to the surface by elongation of its perianth tube. The Sea Wrack, *Zostera marina*, has pollen grains which are long and slender filaments, and these are released in the water and remain submerged while they drift to the projecting stigmas.

Less usual pollinating agents are snails and slugs, which crawl over the inconspicuous brown flowers of the familiar *Aspidistra elatior*; and bats, which have been described as pollinating flowers of certain tropical trees, visiting them for the sake of the copiously secreted nectar.

Self-pollination: Cleistogamy: Self-sterility.

It has already been stated that there are few plants in which the possibility is quite excluded that the stigmas may receive pollen from anthers of the same flower. If anthers and stigmas are mature at the same time this can easily take place during the visits of insects, unless prevented by special structural features. In very many plants it can occur spontaneously, in absence of insect visits, by the contact of anthers and stigma by pollen falling on the stigmas or by some other means. It is often only towards the close of flowering that self-pollination becomes possible, by an inward curve or growth in length of the stamen filaments or a curvature of the style bringing anthers and stigmas together. In some small and inconspicuous flowers it is possible from the first. Shepherd's purse, *Capsella Bursa-pastoris*, is a familiar example. The tiny white flowers have six stamens, the two outer ones short and the four inner ones long. There are nectaries on each side of the two short stamens, four in all. There is no dichogamy and the anthers of the long stamens are in contact with the stigmas, or nearly so, when dehiscence commences. Insects visit the flowers occasionally, and then may effect cross-pollination, but self-pollination is automatic and inevitable.

Some plants have, besides normal flowers, flowers which do not open at all and are regularly self-pollinated to the complete exclusion of crossing. Such flowers are called cleistogamous, and are found in the Sweet Violet, *Viola odorata*, Wood Sorrel, *Oxalis acetosella*, Sundews, *Drosera*, and several other plants. The corolla is usually little developed and the anthers do not dehisce, but the pollen grains germinate while still inside, their tubes piercing the anther-wall to reach the stigma. Good seed is set without fail, often much more than in the ovaries of the normally opening flowers.

In some flowers no seed is set in absence of insect visits, even though it can be seen that self-pollen has reached the stigmas. This phenomenon is called self-sterility, and is by no means infrequent. Thus the common Red Poppy, *Papaver Rhoeas*, and the Meadow Buttercup, *Ranunculus acris* (Fig. 54), have both been described as self-sterile, although this seems not to be true of all individuals of either species. Other familiar examples are Red and White Clover, *Trifolium pratense* and *T. repens*, Madonna Lily, *Lilium candidum*, and many orchids. The reason for self-sterility is sometimes that the pollen is killed before germinating, sometimes that the pollen-tubes start normally but soon cease to grow. A third cause operative in Laburnum, *Cytisus Laburnum*, is that no pollen can germinate until the stigma has been rubbed sufficiently hard to rupture some of the papillae. This takes place if an insect visits the flower, after which either self-pollen or pollen from another flower germinates readily.

The flowers of some varieties of pears, cherries, and plums are sterile not only to their own pollen but to pollen of any other flower of the same variety. It is necessary, therefore, to plant a few trees of another variety in orchards of these self-sterile varieties. The reasons for this peculiarity are obscure but are doubtless related to the complicated history and interrelations of the varieties involved.

Significance of Cross-pollination.

It must occur to every one who examines flowers to inquire why it should be that so many flowers show elaborate contrivances resulting probably, but not inevitably, in cross-pollination, when self-pollination could take place quite certainly by very simple adjustments in the position of anthers and stigmas. This is a question which can at present be answered only in part. It must first be realized that pollination is merely a preliminary to fertilization, the union of a male sexual cell or gamete with a female gamete. The problem is, then, why cross-fertilization should be contrived rather than self-fertilization.

It is evident that two gametes are much more likely to be different genetically if they come from two different parent plants than if they come from the same plant. The product of their fusion, the embryo plant of the next generation, has therefore a much greater chance of being different from its parents and from any of the parent generation, 'better' or 'worse', if it results from cross-pollination rather than self-pollination. There is a great mortality amongst seeds and seedlings: all are submitted to the sifting process called Natural Selection and only a very small percentage ever reaches reproductive maturity. The 'better' plants are those whose genetical constitution gives them a greater chance than others of becoming adult plants and setting good seed. Our argument leads to the conclusion, then, that since only a few of the 'best' individuals of each generation survive, products of cross-pollination will on the whole be parents of a greater proportion of the next generation than the products of self-pollination. If features facilitating cross-pollination are inherited, this is equivalent to saying that such features tend to persist, and that the plants exhibiting them gradually oust those that do not, for the total number of individuals in a species does not vary very greatly. There is an additional factor operating in the same direction, that products of cross-pollination are not only more variable but, as Darwin showed, often have a higher average vigour than products of self-pollination. This phenomenon is known as 'hybrid vigour', and is imperfectly understood, but it evidently increases the chance that the surviving 'best' individuals which form the next generation shall be products of cross-pollination.

The above argument applies to the products of cross- and self-fertilization in other kinds of plants and in animals, and in still greater force to the products of sexual as compared with asexual reproduction. Asexual reproduction involves no machinery tending to produce progeny different from the parents other than by the spontaneous occurrence of mutations, and its products will be at a disadvantage compared with products of any type of sexual reproduction.

In cross-pollinated types there is always an element of uncertainty. Appropriate types of insects may fail to visit the flower, or if they do arrive, they may transfer no pollen grains from another flower. Pollination by wind would seem to be still more uncertain. The advantages which accrue from a mechanism for cross-pollination are evidently dependent upon the efficiency of the mechanism. A self-pollinated flower which sets plenty of seed may be 'better' than a cross-pollinated flower which sets very little seed. This consideration enables us to understand why many flowers are so constructed that an opportunity is first provided for cross-pollination by insects to take place, but later self-pollination is almost inevitable, so that plenty of seed is set even in absence of insect visits. Interesting examples are known of flowers which do not possess this safeguarding possibility of self-pollination and which seldom set seed because insects for whose visits they are strictly specialized have become rare. Amongst British plants the Greater Bindweed, *Calystegia sepium*, has a very long corolla-tube and only the Convolvulus Hawkmoth, *Sphinx convolvuli*, normally visits it for nectar. The moth is now rare in this country, and the flowers produce seed only as an occasional result of visits by other insects. In contrast with this, *Compositae*, such as Dandelion, have nectar accessible to a great variety of insects so that the flowers are generally cross-pollinated. Most of them can also be self-pollinated if insect visits fail, and large quantities of good seed are produced regularly. This may be regarded as an example of a highly efficient, though not highly specialized, pollination mechanism.

A problem which is not quite satisfactorily solved is whether cross-pollination of two flowers of the same plant confers any advantages compared with self-pollination. This sort of crossing must take place very frequently since insects normally visit flower after flower of one plant before passing to another plant. It is not obvious that male gametes and eggs from different flowers of the same plant should differ from each other to any greater extent than if they came from the same flower, since the parent cells of all are identical, but it would be valuable to have the matter more closely investigated.

IV

FERTILIZATION: THE SEED

WHEN pollen grains arrive on a receptive stigma they may consist of a single cell with one nucleus which soon divides, or their nucleus may already have divided. In either case, they eventually contain two nuclei, one called the tube nucleus and the other the generative nucleus. The latter is surrounded by a sheath of dense cytoplasm, so that a naked generative cell lies within the original cell. The grains soon germinate in the sugary solution secreted by the papillae of a mature stigma. Germination consists in the emergence of one or more slender pollen-tubes through thin spots in the outer wall of the grain. The tube nucleus moves to the tip of the tube, which passes down between the stigmatic papillae and then down intercellular spaces between the loosely packed cells of the style. Eventually it reaches the ovary where it passes either down the central axis or in the outer wall until it is close to an ovule. Then it emerges from the wall and grows down the micropyle of the ovule, attracted by some chemical secretion. Ovules are generally arranged with their micropyles close to a wall, so that no air-gap un-bridged by a film of water has to be traversed by the tube. Meanwhile the generative nucleus, which has remained near the tip of the tube behind the tube nucleus, has divided into two long and slender male nuclei. When the tube reaches the embryo-sac its tip perforates the wall of the sac, passes the synergidae and opens to liberate the three nuclei. The tube nucleus disorganizes and one male nucleus fuses with the ovum while the other fuses with the two central nuclei. The first fusion, of a male nucleus with the ovum or egg, constitutes the true sexual fusion, the fertilization of the egg, and the further development of the fertilized egg gives rise to the embryo or young plant of the next generation. The second fusion is peculiar in that three original nuclei are involved in it. All three may fuse simultaneously—triple fusion—or the two central nuclei may already have united before the male nucleus arrives. The resulting nucleus soon divides and its products acquire cytoplasm and walls to form a tissue, the endosperm, which with the embryo fills the embryo-sac. Meanwhile the synergidae and antipodal cells are becoming disorganized.

Unless these two fusions occur the ovules eventually shrivel and die, even if pollination has taken place. Thus, although pollination is an indispensable preliminary, it is fertilization that is the essential process in the formation of an embryo. An ovule which contains an embryo is termed a seed.

Immediately after fertilization the fusion-nuclei divide repeatedly.

The fertilized egg divides in a characteristic manner to form a chain of cells of which the one at the micropylar end becomes very large and swollen. This cell and all the others except the one at the far end constitute the suspensor. The embryo is formed almost entirely from the end cell remote from the micropyle. Stages in its further development in Shepherd's Purse, *Capsella Bursa-Pastoris*, are shown in Fig. 10. It will be seen that repeated divisions give rise to a multicellular structure which gradually becomes two-lobed, the lobes representing the two first leaves or cotyledons of the embryo. The growing-point of the stem arises between them and the root at the other or micropylar end. The last cell of the suspensor contributes towards the formation of the root-tip.

Meanwhile the other fusion-nucleus has also divided many times. At first no cell-walls are formed, but later cellulose walls divide the endosperm into uninucleate compartments, and further divisions are normal.

The ovule has from the first been connected through its stalk or funicle with the placenta of the ovary, and a vascular strand in the funicle is connected with strands in the ovary, and ultimately with the vascular system of the receptacle. It is therefore possible for water and food materials in solution to pass from the parent plant into the embryo-sac. Part of the food is utilized at once in the formation of protoplasm and cell-walls and as material for respiration, and part is stored. In some seeds, called endospermic, the endosperm persists as a food-storing tissue, but in others, non-endospermic seeds, the food originally in the endosperm is gradually passed into the embryo where it is stored in the cotyledons. The Castor-oil seed, *Ricinus*, is an example of the former, and the Broad Bean, *Vica Faba*, of the latter type of seed.

The development of the embryo does not continue indefinitely. Cell-divisions gradually diminish in frequency and ultimately cease when the embryo has one or two well-formed cotyledons, a tiny stem apex, and a little root. Concurrently with this cessation of cell-division, a progressive loss of water takes place. The outer coat, consisting of one or two integuments, becomes very hard, and eventually the seed separates from the placenta. When this occurs the seed may be termed ripe. If an endospermic seed is dissected at this stage, the small embryo will be found lying in endosperm, the cells of which will be seen to contain fat droplets or starch grains and granules of protein. The water content of the ripe seed is very low, and the food store is chiefly in the form of these insoluble substances, very little sugar or amino-acid being detectable. A non-endospermic seed is similar except that the embryo occupies almost the whole of the interior, the insoluble food substances being stored chiefly in the cotyledons, and the endosperm being scarcely visible as a dry crushed layer just inside the seed coat.

The seed is said now to be in its resting condition, and no obvious changes occur until the beginning of germination.

While all these changes have been taking place in the ovule, changes in the ovary and elsewhere have been resulting in the maturation of the fruit, the structure which contains the ripe seeds.

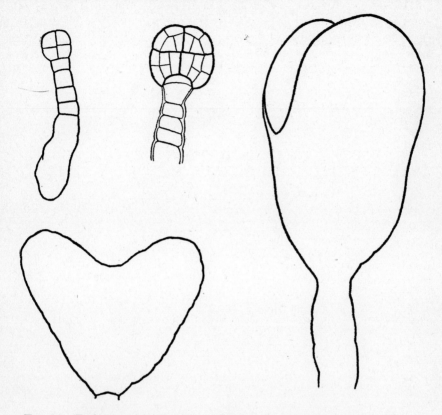

FIG. 10. (Redrawn after Hanstein.) Stages in development of the embryo
of Shepherd's Purse, *Capsella Bursa-Pastoris* Moench

The youngest stage (top left) shows the large basal cell, the suspensor, and the embryo,
consisting of only eight cells. The latest stage (right) shows the two seed-leaves or
cotyledons. The young stem-apex lies between them, and the first root develops at the
junction of the embryo with the suspensor

V

FRUITS

Introduction.

As a result of fertilization profound changes take place in the ovary and also, very often, in adjacent parts such as the perianth, bracts, or receptacle. These changes constitute the formation of the fruit, the structure which encloses the seeds until they are ripe, and by its subsequent behaviour largely determines their mode of dispersal.

An invariable result of fertilization is the enlargement of the ovary, which may attain several thousand times its size at the time of pollination. Thus the inferior ovary of an apple flower has a diameter of 3–4 mm., and the ripe fruit a diameter of about 100 mm. Assuming the ovary to be spherical throughout, the volume increases 25,000-fold. A less extreme example is provided by the Wild Arum, *Arum maculatum*, where the ovary enlarges about 80-fold in the formation of the fruit.

Many fruits consist only of the ovary or, as in the Raspberry, *Rubus Idaeus*, of a cluster of ovaries derived from one flower, but where other organs also become modified so as to assist in the protection of the developing seeds or in their dispersal, they are usually regarded as parts of the fruit. Thus the much enlarged succulent receptacle of the Strawberry and Rose, the tuft of hairs representing the calyx and enabling the fruits of the Thistle and Dandelion to be carried long distances in the wind, the cupules completely enclosing the developing ovaries of Beech and Sweet Chestnut, are all parts of the fruit. So, too, are the swollen succulent end of the flower-stalk of Cashew nut, *Anacardium occidentale*, and the enlarged persistent calyx of Sál, *Shorea robusta*. In Pineapple, *Ananas sativa*, the axis of the inflorescence, the bracts, the perianth, and the inferior ovaries all combine to form one large succulent mass, and the whole is a single fruit since it acts as a unit in the protection and dispersal of the seeds.

The stimulus to further development is usually fertilization, but sometimes, as in many Orchids, the ovary begins to enlarge after pollination, a fruit being formed even in the absence of fertilization. This takes place, too, in many cultivated races of bananas and oranges which have no seeds. For the most part, however, the whole flower and its associated structures wither and fall when fertilization fails to take place, even if the stigma has been pollinated.

Types of Fruits.

In describing the different kinds of fruits it is convenient to divide them into two main groups, dry fruits and succulent fruits, the names being descriptive of their condition when ripe. There is no very sharp line of distinction between the classes. All fruits are somewhat succulent in early stages, and some, like those of the Marsh Marigold, *Caltha palustris*, and Snowdrop, *Galanthus nivalis*, remain succulent until they open and only then become dry. On the whole, however, it is not difficult to allocate fruits to one or other of the groups.

Dry Fruits.

The fruit of the Christmas Rose, *Helleborus niger*, will serve as an example of a simple and probably primitive type of dry fruit. Every flower forms a cluster of about five fruits, one from each apocarpous ovary. After pollination the persistent sepals turn green and the ovaries increase in length from about 10 mm. to nearly 20 mm., their breadth increasing proportionately. When increase in size has ceased the ovary wall begins to dry, and, as a result of tensions set up in the drying tissues, eventually splits down the vertical groove facing the centre of the flower, exposing the ripe seeds still attached to the inside edges of the groove. The fruit-stalk is curved so that the fruits are held obliquely, and as the seeds become detached they fall to the ground. The fruits may close again in damp air but reopen when it becomes dry, these movements being the result of hygroscopic curvatures of the dead walls. Here the fruit is derived from a single superior carpel, is dry at maturity, and splits or **dehisces** along the ventral side to expose the ripe seeds. The fruits of the Columbine, *Aquilegia*, Monkshood, *Aconitum*, and Garden Delphinium, *Delphinium* (Fig. 13), are closely similar and all are called **follicles.** The fruits of Marsh Marigold, *Caltha*, differ in being still green and succulent when they open, but they dry later and are also called follicles.

The pods of the Pea family, *Leguminosae*, resemble follicles in being derived from single apocarpous superior ovaries, but since they differ in splitting along two lines, both back and front, they are distinguished as **legumes.**

Of the flowers with superior ovaries very many give rise to dry fruits called **capsules.** These resemble follicles and legumes in being dry and dehiscent, but differ in being derived from syncarpous ovaries. They usually dehisce by slits which may either extend from apex to base, forming a number of more or less widely divergent valves, or may reach only a short distance down from the apex to form small teeth. In multi-locular capsules the slits may be along the mid-lines of the outer walls of the loculi, so that each valve consists of half the outer wall of two adjacent loculi with the intervening partition to which the seeds are attached, as in Bluebell, *Scilla*; or the loculi may separate from each other as in Figwort, *Scrophularia* (Fig. 11), and Foxglove, *Digitalis*, where the axile placentae, with seeds still attached, are left standing in the

FIG. 11. *Scrophularia aquatica* L. ×5

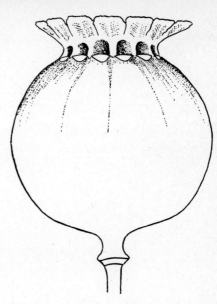

FIG. 12. *Papaver somniferum* L. ×3

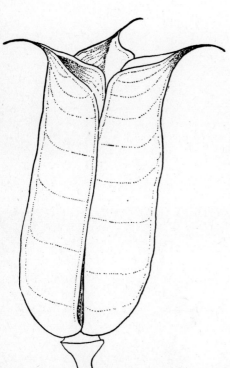

FIG. 13. Delphinium ×5

FIG. 14. *Sarothamnus scoparius*
Wimm. ×3

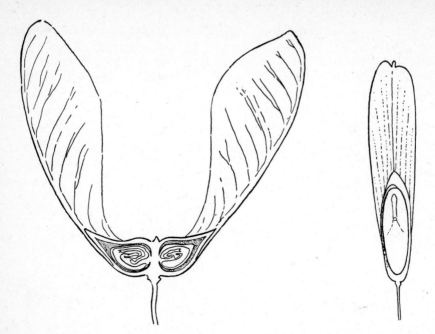

FIG. 15. *Acer Pseudoplatanus* L. ×2   FIG. 16. *Fraxinus excelsior* L. ×2

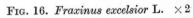

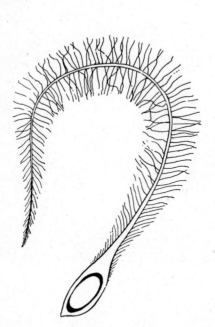

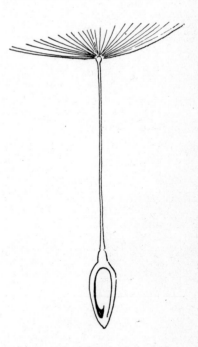

FIG. 17. *Clematis Vitalba* L. ×5   FIG. 18. *Taraxacum officinale* L. ×5

centre. The Sweet Violet, *Viola odorata*, has unilocular capsules and dehiscence is along lines midway between the placentae, so that each of the three valves carries two or more rows of seeds down its centre. The capsules of Primrose, *Primula vulgaris*, and White Campion, *Melandrium album*, open by ten short teeth which curl back in dry weather but straighten so as to close the capsule again when the air is damp; and those of Poppy, *Papaver*, by a row of small holes just beneath the flat top.

Members of the Wallflower family, *Cruciferae*, have specialized capsules, the two valves separating, from below upwards, from a central framework to which the seeds remain attached. When the valves are long and narrow as in Wallflower, *Cheiranthus*, the fruit is called a siliqua, and when short and broad a silicula. The valves of siliculae may be flat as in the very large siliculae of Honesty, *Lunaria*, or strongly concave, as in Shepherd's Purse, *Capsella*, the central framework being broad in Honesty but very narrow in Shepherd's Purse.

Most dry fruits with only a single seed and a few with more than one seed fail to split in any definite way but merely open irregularly after they have reached the ground, where the tissues of the wall are softened by the combined action of the weather and of bacteria. The **achenes** of Buttercup, *Ranunculus*, Meadow Rue, *Thalictrum*, and Old Man's Beard, *Clematis* (Fig. 17), are one-seeded indehiscent dry fruits formed from single superior ovaries, borne in clusters in all three genera, since all have numerous ovaries in each flower. The fruits of grasses are similar but have the single seed closely adherent to the wall, and only one is formed from each flower.

The **nut** differs from the achene only in having a very hard outer wall, and the four separating one-seeded parts of the ovary of White Dead-nettle, *Lamium album*, may be given this name.

All the fruits so far mentioned are derived from superior ovaries, but there is a parallel series of fruits derived from inferior ovaries, often distinguished by prefixing the word **inferior.** Thus the Daffodil, *Narcissus*, Crocus, and Iris have inferior capsules, dehiscing by slits midway between the septa; and in Canterbury Bell, *Campanula*, the inferior capsule opens by apical pores. Dandelion, *Taraxacum*, Cornflower, *Centaurea*, and Summer Chrysanthemum, all members of the *Compositae*, have fruits which may be called inferior achenes, since they are one-seeded, indehiscent, and dry, but formed from an inferior ovary. The separating halves of the inferior fruit of Hogweed, *Heracleum*, and other Umbellifers are also one-seeded and indehiscent and again may be termed inferior achenes. Finally many fruits are inferior nuts, the nuts of Beech, Oak, Sweet Chestnut, and Hazel all falling in this class. It is interesting to note that Horse Chestnuts are seeds borne in a dehiscent capsule, and thus not really comparable with the inferior one-seeded nuts of Sweet Chestnut, though the spiny cupule of the latter may easily be mistaken for the wall of a capsule.

SUCCULENT FRUITS.

The simplest type of succulent fruit is the **berry,** which may be derived either from a superior or an inferior ovary. The fruit-wall becomes soft and juicy, consisting almost entirely of large, thin-walled cells, and during development it obliterates the loculi and envelopes the seeds. The fruits of Wild Arum, *Arum maculatum*, Orange, *Citrus Aurantium*, and Tomato, *Solanum Lycopersicum* (Fig. 20), are examples of superior berries, while those of Honeysuckle, *Lonicera*, Currants and Gooseberry, *Ribes*, Banana, *Musa*, and Cucumber, *Cucumis*, are inferior berries.

The **drupe** differs from a berry in having a two-layered fruit-wall, an outer fleshy layer and an inner stony layer. The Plum (Fig. 21) is a good example. Here the epidermis forms a skin covering the fleshy layer of the wall, while the stony layer with the enclosed seed or 'kernel', is the familiar 'stone'. The Cherry, Peach, and Apricot are similar, and are all superior drupes. The Walnut is an inferior drupe. The Coconut, too, is usually classed as a drupe, since the broad, fibrous layer and the stony 'nut' are comparable with the fleshy and stony layers of the Plum, but here the ripe fruit is dry, not succulent. Some drupes have more than one seed, as in the fruits of Holly (*Ilex*), where the fleshy layer encloses four 'stones', each with a seed inside.

The fruits of Apple (Fig. 22), Pear, Quince, and allied plants form a special class called **pomes.** Here the wall of the inferior ovary becomes enormously enlarged and remains succulent, while a tough membranous layer surrounds the loculi in which the seeds lie, this central part being called the 'core'. The 'haw' of Hawthorn, *Crataegus*, is similar, but the 1–3 loculi develop stony walls.

In many fruits the succulent part is not the wall, or part of the wall, of the ovary, but is derived from some associated structure. Such fruits may be termed **false fruits.** Examples are the Strawberry, in which small achenes are borne on a much swollen conical receptacle; the 'hip' of Rose (Fig. 19), in which the succulent receptacle is urn-shaped, with the numerous achenes borne on its inner wall; the Fig where the fleshy structure represents a whole inflorescence-axis bearing numerous whole flowers on its inner wall; and the Pineapple, where the massive succulent fruit consists of inflorescence-axis, bracts, and perianth as well as the inferior ovaries of the numerous flowers. These, it should be noted, make an exact definition of 'fruit' difficult, since the individual achenes of the Strawberry, for example, might be called fruits, as well as the whole structure consisting of the receptacle with numerous achenes. It seems best, however, to use the term for the structure which acts as a

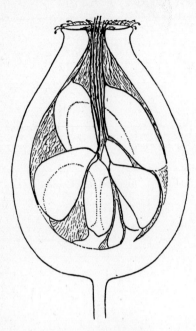

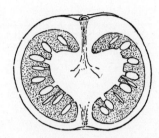

FIG. 20. Tomato

FIG. 19. Rose hip

FIG. 21
Plum (stone in black)

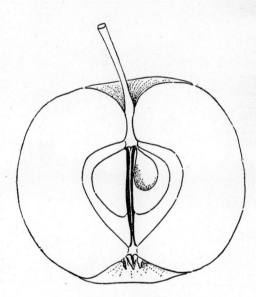

FIG. 22. Apple

unit in protection and dispersal of the seeds. Then the whole Strawberry is the fruit, in agreement with popular usage.

Dispersal.

DRY FRUITS.

When a dry fruit dehisces the seeds may either drop to the soil at once or may be shaken out gradually as the fruit-stalk is swayed in the wind. How far away the seeds drop depends upon the height of the fruit above the soil, the length and flexibility of its stalk, and the lightness of its seeds. Many fall close to the parent plant, but in a strong wind some may be carried considerable distances before reaching the ground. Dry, indehiscent fruits are usually detached and dispersed in the same way, carrying the seed inside them to be released later when the fruit wall rots away. Of the thirty plants whose flowers are described in this book about two-thirds are dispersed in this rather casual manner, and this may be fairly close to the proportion of all Flowering Plants which lack a specialized dispersal mechanism. The Christmas Rose, *Helleborus*; Marsh Marigold, *Caltha*; Garden Delphinium, *Delphinium*; Monkshood, *Aconitum*; Columbine, *Aquilegia*; Sweet Violet, *Viola*; White Campion, *Melandrium*; Primrose, *Primula*; Plantain, *Plantago*; Figwort, *Scrophularia*; Foxglove, *Digitalis*; Bluebell, *Scilla*; all have dry, dehiscent fruits. In the Violet the seeds are detached by the inrolling of the walls of the capsule-valves and fall in a cluster to the ground, but in all the others they are retained within the open fruit until shaken out by the wind or tipped out by bending of the fruit-stalk. The achenes of the Buttercup, *Ranunculus*, and Meadow Rue, *Thalictrum*, are similarly shaken to the ground and so are the nutlets of the White Deadnettle, *Lamium*, and the inferior achenes of the Cornflower, *Centaurea*, and the Summer Chrysanthemum, *Chrysanthemum*.

Dehiscence by apical pores, as in Poppy, *Papaver* (Fig. 12), and Bellflower, *Campanula*, or by hygroscopic teeth as in Campion, *Melandrium*, to form a kind of censer, provides some degree of regulation of the rate at which seeds are shed, increasing the chance that some may remain to be flung long distances by an especially strong wind.

An interesting deviation from the ordinary behaviour of capsules is seen in the fruits of Snowdrop, *Galanthus*, and Crocus, where the fruit-stalk elongates considerably and then collapses so that the capsules lie on the ground and shed their seeds some little distance from the parent plant.

Many dry fruits dehisce so violently that the seeds are flung considerable distances. This is true of the little siliqua of the Hairy Bitter Cress, *Cardamine hirsuta*, and of many legumes such as those of Broom, *Sarothamnus* (Fig. 14), and Gorse, *Ulex*, where the strains set up in the fruit-wall during gradual drying are released suddenly in dehiscence, the two halves becoming spirally twisted and flinging the seeds for distances up to 12 feet. The cracks of splitting Gorse-pods can often be plainly heard on hot days in summer. A rather more specialized type of violent dehiscence is seen in the fruits of Meadow Cranesbill, *Geranium pratense*, where five strips of surface tissue of the much elongated style become suddenly detached from below, simultaneously or one at a time. Each drags with it one of the separating loculi of the ovary, coils up like a spring and flings the seeds 3 to 6 feet away.

In many species of *Viola*, though not in the Sweet Violet, the valves of the capsule, after dehiscence, gradually curve inwards as drying continues and the smooth shiny seeds are suddenly shot out to distances of 4 to 6 feet in much the same way as orange pips can be shot from between the fingers.

In other fruits the seeds are modified so that they are carried considerable distances by the wind. Thus the extremely minute seeds of Orchids and Heathers and the somewhat larger seeds of Stinging Nettle are so light that they remain suspended for long periods, meanwhile being carried far from the parent plants. The seeds of Willows and Poplars and of Willowherbs, *Epilobium*, have tufts of hairs at one end, and those of Trumpet Creeper, *Campsis radicans*, lateral wings, two structural modifications which give a much increased resistance to falling and result in wide dispersal. Some indehiscent fruits have analogous modifications. Thus the achenes of Old Man's Beard, *Clematis* (Fig. 17), are surmounted by the long, hairy style; the inferior achenes of Thistle and Dandelion by a ring of hairs representing the calyx; and the fruits of Ash (Fig. 16), Sycamore (Fig. 15), and Elm have wings which are outgrowths of the ovary wall. Other structures may be utilized as wings. In Hornbeam the wing consists of three bracteoles concrescent at their base, and in Lime one of the bracteoles of the terminal flower, much enlarged, acts as a wing for a cluster of fruits. The separating halves of the fruit of Hogweed, *Heracleum*, may also be placed in this category since they are much flattened and have winged margins.

There remains for consideration dispersal by animals. Many small seeds are carried in haphazard fashion in the coats of animals and amongst the feathers of birds, or still more commonly in soil adhering to their feet. Hazelnuts, beechnuts, acorns, and other fruits with a hard outer shell are sometimes dropped from the beaks of flying birds, or stored and forgotten by squirrels and rats. Some fruits, however, are more specialized in the possession of hooks or spines which become entangled in the coats of passing animals. Examples are provided by the fruits of Cleavers, *Galium aparine*, which are covered with little recurved hooks, the achenes of Wood Avens, *Geum urbanum*, with hooked persistent styles, and the burrs of Burdock, *Arctium*, where the whole 'head' is detached, the involucral bracts serving as hooks.

A few fruits are dispersed by water currents. These usually have walls containing large air-filled spaces so that they float readily. Familiar examples are the fruits of Water-lilies.

SUCCULENT FRUITS.

The developing seeds have to be protected from water-loss before they are ready for dispersal, and features originally protective in function may later become modified so that they aid dispersal. Succulence of the young fruit provides the seeds with a thick water-jacket. If the succulence persists after the seeds become ripe dispersal may take place in two ways. Large fruits like apples fall to the ground and the seeds are released only when the wall rots. Removal from the vicinity of the parent may occur when animals trample or eat the fruits, but there is no special mechanism for dispersal. Before falling these fruits may change from green to a bright yellow or red colour, and then are conspicuous to birds and may be pecked by them. This change of colour is much more pronounced and is associated with a higher sugar-content and therefore a greater palatability in such small succulent fruits as those of Cherry, Raspberry, Strawberry, Rose, Currant, Honeysuckle, and very many others. These are swallowed whole by birds, and their seeds, being resistant to grinding in the gizzard and to digestive juices, are eventually excreted unharmed and thus very effectively dispersed. The combination of characters, bright colour, succulence, sugar-content, and resistant seeds constitutes a very high degree of specialization for bird dispersal, and fruits of this kind have come to be a most important part of the food of many small birds.

VI

THE PRACTICAL EXAMINATION OF FLOWERS

THE full understanding of a plant's reproductive mechanism is only to be obtained flower in hand, and the best use of the descriptions that follow can only be made in the laboratory. They will be most useful as an illustrated guide to structures under direct observation rather than as an arm-chair substitute for the flowers themselves. The examination should be carried out systematically, beginning with what is obvious and working down to points that are more obscure.

Dissection.

Note first the arrangement of the individual flowers in the inflorescence, and the position and number of flowers which are open at the same time.

The orientation of the flower, i.e. its arrangement relative to the stalk of the inflorescence, is a matter of some importance, and is usually easy to see in irregular flowers, but may be rather difficult when the petals and sepals are all fairly equal in shape and size. Sometimes the flower stalks take on slight twists that depend mainly on external circumstances, and the original arrangement can only be discovered in sections of the young inflorescence specially prepared while it is still enclosed in a bud.

Individual flowers are best examined by cutting them in half vertically in the antero-posterior plane, i.e. the scalpel must pass through the middle of the floral member (petal or sepal) that is at the back (posterior) or nearest to the stalk from which it comes off, and also through the member opposite to this, the front (anterior) member. Nearly all flowers are symmetrical about this plane. Zygomorphic flowers are symmetrical about no other plane, so no difficulty exists in discovering it in flowers of this class. In radially symmetrical (actinomorphic) flowers more care must be exercised, and when doubts arise reference must be made to the following drawings. Several flowers must be cut, choosing specimens at various stages of development. This is particularly important with flowers whose anthers and stigmas ripen at different times. When a drawing is to be made the stage of development to be drawn should be chosen with care, and occasionally more than one illustration will be advisable. To examine the cut surfaces thoroughly, especially in the region of the ovary, a good lens with a magnification of about ten diameters is necessary. This is a rather higher magnification than that of many lenses which are sold for the purpose but are not really suitable.

Drawing.

It is useless to draw isolated organs of the flower, since the arrangement of the floral parts is quite as important as their individual structures. Both arrangement and structure are best illustrated by means of a ground plan and median elevation of the flower as a whole. The median elevation is drawn as seen in a half-flower cut in the median plane as already described. It has been found that it is best to conventionalize the ground plan into the form of a floral diagram. This represents the arrangement of the floral parts on a series of concentric circles, with the ovary in the centre and the sepals outside. Agreed symbols are used to represent carpels, stamens, petals, sepals, &c., and their relations can be shown with fair accuracy. In this book the original conventions suggested by Eichler are used in the somewhat modified forms employed by Church. Either a sepal or petal is always represented as being exactly at the back of the flower and the arrangement of the other parts settled in relation to this.

Floral Diagram.

A floral diagram is constructed by deciding first how many whorls of organs there are and drawing the appropriate number of concentric circles. The position of the main stalk or axis is shown by a small circle enclosing a cross, placed above the main circles, and the position of the leaf or bract subtending the flower is shown by its appropriate symbol below. The individual organs are inserted on their proper circles having regard to their placing, the method of their overlapping, if any, and other special features for which the individual illustrations must be consulted.

Median Elevation.

The only convention to be observed here is that the face drawn should agree accurately with the antero-posterior plane of the floral diagram, which should have been constructed first. It is usual to draw the half of the flower corresponding with the right-hand side of the floral diagram. The drawing should be large and bold, that is to say it should occupy a whole page and be finished off with firm lines, special care being taken to avoid fuzziness in the central parts. Shading should be used very sparingly if at all, since the usual effect is to obscure rather than clarify. For the same reason colouring, although an essential part of the flower's make-up, is better not attempted ; written notes must be made to suffice. The principal dimensions of the flower should be measured and the drawing carried out approximately to scale, a note being made of the magnification intended. For a practical example of the style of drawing advised see the illustration of a plantain flower (Fig. 70).

In a laboratory drawing it is a good plan to label all the parts of the flower in a neat and systematic fashion, especially those that are peculiar to the individual flower under examination or that are otherwise remarkable. The position of the nectary is naturally a matter of great importance, and should be clearly shown. It would, of course, be unwise to have the book illustration open in front of you all the time you are making a drawing, but a careful comparison when you have finished would be useful.

Material.

All the flowers discussed in this book can be obtained easily either growing wild or as common garden plants. They flower in the spring and early summer, most of them during the term between the easter and summer holidays. The most likely localities for the wild plants are indicated in the individual descriptions. When using garden plants it is necessary to avoid over-cultured specimens, since rich feeding may lead to an abnormal increase in the number of parts, or even to 'doubling' of the flower, as in roses other than briers, double chrysanthemums, daffodils, &c. All varieties named by horticulturalists *flore pleno* are thus to be avoided: the garden plants chosen in the following illustrations do not double at all readily.

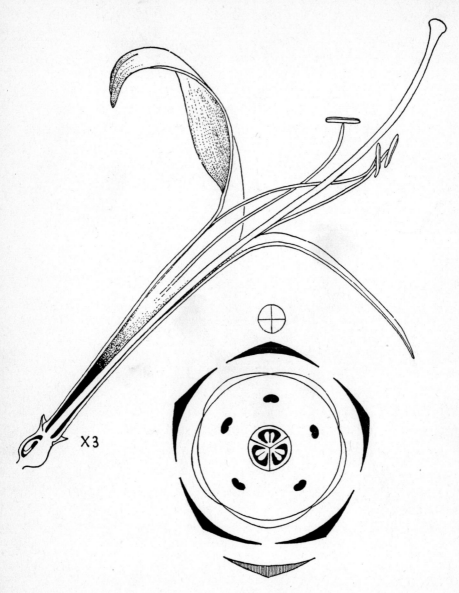

X3

FIG. 23. *Lonicera Periclymenum* L.

VII

DRAWINGS AND DESCRIPTIONS OF SELECTED FLOWERS

LONICERA PERICLYMENUM L.

CAPRIFOLIACEAE

HONEYSUCKLE

Inflorescence: a head of dichasial triads, with a terminal flower. There is a complete set of bracts and bracteoles, those of the central flower of each triad being narrow while the bracteoles of the lateral flowers are broader and concave; all are glandular-hairy.

Flower: hermaphrodite, zygomorphic.

CALYX: five free sepals, small, ovate-obtuse, glandular-hairy.

COROLLA: zygomorphic; sympetalous, with a narrow tube 25–30 mm. long, and a mouth of two lips which are strongly rolled back, the upper broad, ending in four rounded lobes, the lower narrow and entire; tube greenish-yellow, streaked with red outside; lips white or pink, becoming cream then yellow-brown.

ANDROECIUM: five stamens, borne on the corolla-tube opposite the sepals; anthers attached at the middle on long slender filaments, projecting 18–25 mm. from the corolla-tube.

GYNAECIUM: inferior; syncarpous; with three, sometimes two, loculi each with several ovules on axile placentae; style slender, a little longer than the stamens, ending in a stigmatic head with two to four, usually three, papillose areas separated by grooves.

NECTARY: a fleshy ring round the base of the style, and hairs on the inner wall of the corolla-tube.

Fruit: a cluster of red inferior berries.

Status: a native woody climber, common in woods and hedgerows, flowering in June.

The flowers open first at twilight, and are not dichogamous. They are held almost horizontally and in early stages the filaments and style are curved slightly upwards so as to hold the anthers and stigma opposite the entrance to the corolla-tube, the stigma a little beyond the anthers. When the anthers have dehisced the filaments curve downwards. The

G

style also curves downwards, but more slowly than the filaments. Later the stigma turns brown and withers. There is a marked colour-change during flowering, the corolla being ivory-white or pink when first open, then passing through cream to yellowish-brown when the stigma withers.

According to some observers the style is bent down below the stamens in the first stage of flowering, then rises to hold the stigma opposite the corolla-tube after the stamens have dehisced. The flowers appear to behave somewhat differently in different localities.

The corolla-tube being 25–30 mm. long and very narrow, nectar is ordinarily accessible only to long-tongued moths, most of which fly at dusk or by night. They are attracted by the strong fragrance and guided when close by the whitish corollas. In hovering in front of a recently opened flower they strike with their underside first the stigma and then the anthers, and may thus effect cross-pollination. Self-pollination may sometimes take place during withdrawal from the flower. At a later stage they touch only the stigma which is carried downwards less rapidly than the anthers.

During active secretion nectar may rise nearly to the top of the tube and then long-tongued bees such as *Bombus hortorum* can reach it provided they can get an adequate foothold. There is, however, no proper landing-stage, and bees rarely visit many flowers in succession. Their visits, moreover, are usually ineffective through failure to touch the anthers or stigma.

The Honeysuckle is very typical of flowers pollinated by night-flying moths in its pale colour, strong scent, very long and narrow corolla-tube, absence of landing stage, and projecting stamens and style.

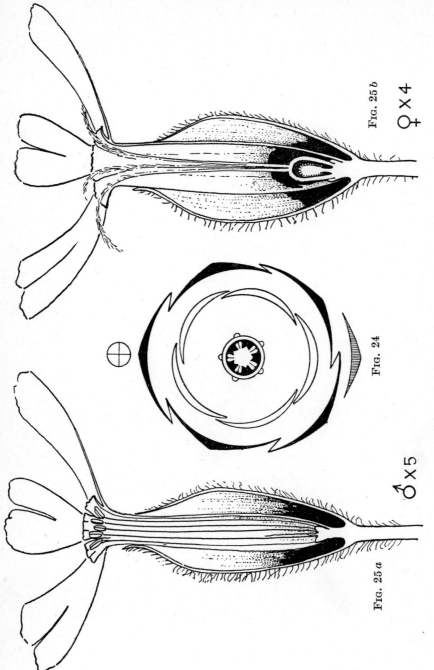

FIG. 25 *b*

♀ × 4

FIG. 24

♂ × 5

FIG. 25 *a*

Melandrium album Garcke

MELANDRIUM ALBUM Garcke. (*LYCHNIS ALBA* Mill.)

CARYOPHYLLACEAE

WHITE CAMPION

Inflorescence: a cyme, dichasial at first but monochasial in later branching; bracts and bracteoles small and narrow, hairy.

Flowers: unisexual (dioecious or polygamous), actinomorphic.

(*a*) STAMINATE FLOWER.

CALYX: pale green, gamosepalous below to form a glandular-hairy tube 12 mm. long, with ten hairy brown-purple ribs. The tube widens upwards, then narrows abruptly and ends in five triangular teeth, 3 mm. long, each with one strong rib.

COROLLA: five free petals arising from the receptacle 2–3 mm. above the base of the calyx tube. The petals have erect, flattened, stalk-like bases (claws) about 3 mm. wide whose sides touch to form a tube about 13 mm. long. At the top of each claw are four little scales 2–3 mm. long, broadening above. These bend outwards to form a corona whose effect is to increase the length of the narrow part of the tube to about 15 mm. The wide part of the petal spreads horizontally outwards from the point of origin of the corona, forming a blade (limb) 12–13 mm. long and gradually widening to about 11 mm. The limb is deeply cut to about 5 mm. from its base. The five limbs make a white lobed plate 25 mm. across.

ANDROECIUM: hypogynous, of ten stamens in two whorls of five, but with so slight a difference in distance from the centre of the flower as to appear to lie in a single whorl unless examined very closely. The outermost are opposite the petals and usually have filaments only 7–8 mm. long, while those opposite the sepals have filaments 13–14 mm. long. The filaments are hairy near the base.

GYNAECIUM: non-functional; a little flattened hairy structure with a hairy filamentous process from its apex.

NECTARY: nectar is secreted from the rudimentary ovary.

(*b*) CARPELLARY FLOWER.

CALYX: larger than the staminate flower, and relatively wider. The over-all length is 20 mm., the lower tubular part being about 14 mm. and the teeth 6 mm. long.

COROLLA: five free petals arising immediately above the calyx, there being no internode as in the staminate flower. The petals have the same form as in the staminate flower but are larger, their claws forming a tube 18 mm. long, or 20 mm. with the corona.

ANDROECIUM: usually absent, but small carpellary flowers may have ten hairy staminodes 1–2 mm. long.

GYNAECIUM: superior, syncarpous; ovary cylindrical, 6 by 3 mm., unilocular with a very large number of tiny ovules between the five ribs of a free central placenta which reaches to 1 mm. from the top of the ovary chamber; five long styles, 18 mm. long, curving outwards over the corona and between the petals; the styles are stigmatic on their upper surface and edges for the upper two-thirds of their length.

NECTARY: nectar is secreted from the base of the ovary and collects in the corolla tube.

(c) HERMAPHRODITE FLOWERS are sometimes found.

Fruit: a capsule dehiscing by twenty teeth each about 3 mm. long. The numerous tiny seeds are scattered when the fruit-stalk is shaken by wind.

Status: a native annual or biennial herb of fields and hedgerows, flowering from June to September.

White Campions are of interest in a number of ways. The flowers are usually unisexual and dioecious but hermaphrodite and staminate flowers are occasionally found together on the same plant. They are pollinated by night-flying moths and show several features which can be related to this fact. Thus they are white and open only at dusk, closing again early in the morning. During the daytime they appear to have withered, the petals being limp and shrunken. Flowers in deep shade may open during the day, but this is unusual. When open at night the petals have a strong fragrance, but this cannot be detected during the day. Nectar is secreted by the ovary or ovary rudiments and collects at the base of a narrow tube about 20 mm. long in the carpellary, and about 15 mm. long in the staminate flowers, lengths which exclude all but the longest-tongued bees and *Lepidoptera*. The fact that the flowers close during the day restricts successful visitors to long-tongued nocturnal moths, since bees and butterflies do not fly at night. The corresponding position of stamens and stigmatic surfaces makes cross-pollination highly probable when moths visit the flower. Self-pollination is excluded by dioecism.

Red Campion, *Melandrium rubrum*, opens by day and is pollinated by humble-bees, hover-flies, and butterflies.

A Smut fungus, *Ustilago antherarum*, frequently attacks White Campion, causing stamens, whose anthers become filled with violet spores, to develop in the carpellary flowers.

ACONITUM NAPELLUS L.

MONKSHOOD

RANUNCULACEAE

Inflorescence: terminal and axillary racemes; bracts narrow, sometimes with three segments; flower-stalks 12–40 mm. long; flowers held almost horizontally.

Flower: hermaphrodite, zygomorphic.

CALYX: five spirally-arranged free sepals, dark blue-purple in colour. The back sepal is strongly concave and stands erect as a hood 22 mm. high, over the rest of the flower. The side pair towards the back are about 16 mm. long and 17 mm. wide. They curve inwards and touch along part of their upper edges, beneath the hood. The front pair are small, 14 mm. by 6 mm., and are directed forwards and downwards.

COROLLA: about seven free petals. The two at the back consist of long stalks, 15 mm. long, gradually widening into stout spurs, held almost horizontally with blunt upwardly directed tips. There is a flap at the mouth of each spur, hanging vertically downwards with uprolled end. Both petals are enclosed by

FIG. 26. *Aconitum Napellus* L.

the hood, their stalks erect and holding the spurs just under the top of the hood. The stalks are blue-purple and the spurs almost black outside but green inside. The remaining petals, variable in number but usually five, are small and slender, 1–4 mm. long, and are blue-purple in colour.

ANDROECIUM: hypogynous, of about sixty free spirally-arranged stamens; filaments blue, lengthening to about 6 mm., broadened and paler below; anthers small, greenish-blue, dehiscing towards the outside.

GYNAECIUM: superior, of three to five free carpels; ovary 4–5 mm. long, unilocular with several ovules in two rows on the inner side, tapering into a style 4 mm. long, with small terminal stigma.

NECTARY: nectar is secreted in the blunt end of each petal-spur, and collects into a large drop which hangs in the mouth of the spur.

Fruit: three to five dry follicles dehiscing along their inner sides.

Status: a native perennial herb, very local in occurrence; much culti-vated in gardens; flowers in June.

The flowers are held with the three back sepals vertical and the stamens and carpels horizontal. They are protandrous, the first stamens to mature being the outermost and development proceeding inwards. The immature stamens are curved back just below their anthers. During maturation they straighten and then curve upwards so that when the anthers are dehiscing they stand in the entrance to the hood formed by the three back sepals. After dehiscence they bend back again but more strongly than before, so that the withering anthers are held near the bases of the filaments. The stigmas become mature after all the stamens have withered. At earlier stages they are hidden by the stamens, but are exposed and upwardly directed when mature. Self-pollination is normally impossible, but occasionally anthers of the inner-most stamens remain in contact with the stigmas while shedding their pollen.

The flowers of the various species of Monkshood have been described as 'humble-bee flowers *par excellence*'. Insects can land on the front and side sepals and stand so that the anthers or stigmas touch their under-sides, but they can reach nectar only if they have a proboscis at least 15 mm. long: the vertical sides of the back sepal effectively prevent short-tongued insects from climbing nearer to the nectary. By far the commonest visitor is the humble-bee, *Bombus hortorum*, with a pro-boscis about 20 mm. long. The dark blue flowers are distinctively coloured to its eyes, and the entrance to the hood formed by the three back sepals is just the size and shape of its body. The under side of its body strikes dehiscing anthers in the earlier stages of flowering and the upturned stigmas in later stages, so that cross-pollination is readily effected.

A few other long-tongued humble-bees are occasional visitors, reach-ing nectar in the usual way, but as in Columbine, *Aquilegia vulgaris* (Fig. 29), short-tongued bees may steal nectar by biting holes through the hood close to the nectaries.

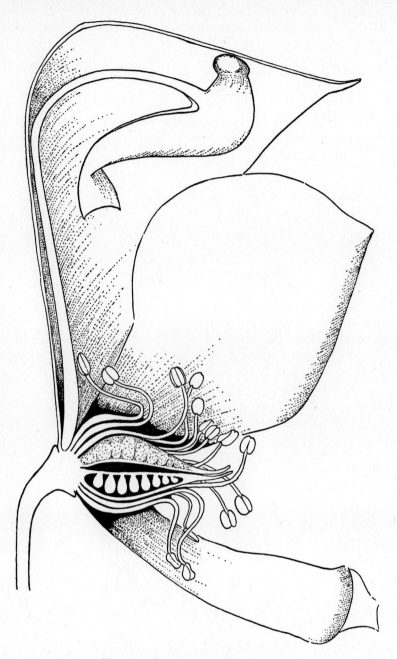

FIG. 27. *Aconitum napellus* L.   ×6

AQUILEGIA VULGARIS L.

RANUNCULACEAE

WILD COLUMBINE

Inflorescence: terminal and axillary cymes; bracts entire or three-lobed; two bracteoles on each flower-stalk; flowers inverted.

Flower: hermaphrodite, actinomorphic.

CALYX: five free, ovate-lanceolate, blue-purple sepals, 20 mm. long, arranged spirally.

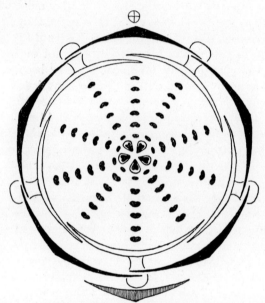

FIG. 28. *Aquilegia vulgaris* L.

COROLLA: five free petals in a whorl, alternating with the sepals. Each petal has a short, oblong blade which stands almost vertical and is prolonged upwards (in the inverted flower) into a long spur, 15–22 mm. long, tapering to its base which is curved inwards towards the flower-stalk. The petals are blue-purple but paler than the sepals.

ANDROECIUM: hypogynous, of about fifty stamens arranged in ten alternating whorls of five. Within the functional stamens there are ten small, narrow, petal-like, sterile stamens or staminodes, in two whorls of five. The anthers dehisce outwards.

GYNAECIUM: superior, of five free carpels; ovary 6 mm. long, slightly curved inwards, hairy, unilocular with two rows of ovules on the inner side. Style lengthening during flowering to 5 mm., grooved on the inner side, stigmatic at its tip.

NECTARY: nectar is secreted at the ends of the spurs, and collects in the incurved tips.

Fruit: five green follicles dehiscing along the inner sides.

Status: a native perennial herb of woods and damp grassland, flowering in June.

The flowers of Wild Columbine are protandrous, the stamens dehiscing in succession from outside inwards. Initially they are curved upwards so that the anthers are at the base of the flower, but they first straighten and then dehisce with the anthers turned slightly outwards towards the petals. The styles are meanwhile elongating and eventually emerge from amongst the stamens, the stigmatic tip now becoming receptive. The flowers hang upside down and are made conspicuous by the blue-purple sepals and petals. The nectar collected at the end of the spur is accessible only to insects with proboscises at least 15 mm. long, and the humble-bee, *Bombus hortorum*, whose proboscis is about 20 mm. long, is the most usual visitor. In visiting a flower it clings from below to the base of a petal and to the cluster of stamens, then thrusts its head into the funnel-shaped entrance of the spur and passes its proboscis along the spur until it reaches the nectar. It normally makes a circuit of the flower, taking nectar from each spur in turn. Meanwhile if the flower is in the staminate stage, the bee is brushing pollen from the outwardly dehiscing anthers. On visiting the flower in the stigmatic stage some of this pollen will be transferred to the outwardly curved stigmas, which project beyond the anthers. Thus cross-pollination may readily be effected, but in the absence of insect visits self-pollination is not excluded, since pollen can fall from the anthers on to the receptive stigmas beneath them.

Short-tongued bees, especially *Bombus terrestris* with proboscis only 3–7 mm. long, sometimes steal nectar by biting through the spurs. Hive-bees may do the same, but more often use the holes already made by *Bombus terrestris*.

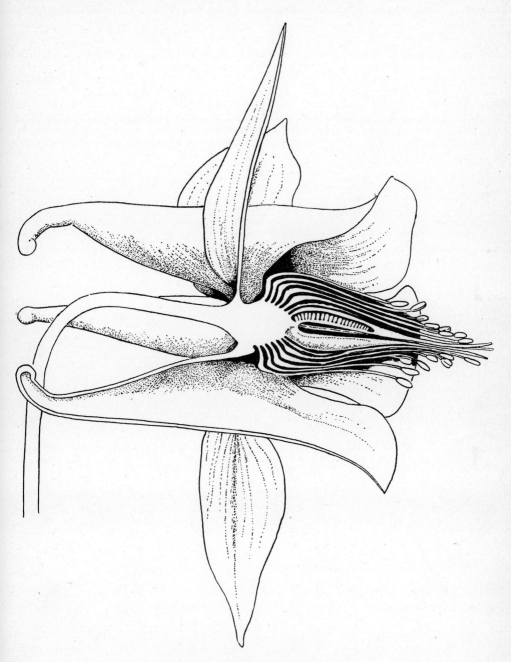

FIG. 29. *Aquilegia vulgaris* L.   ×3

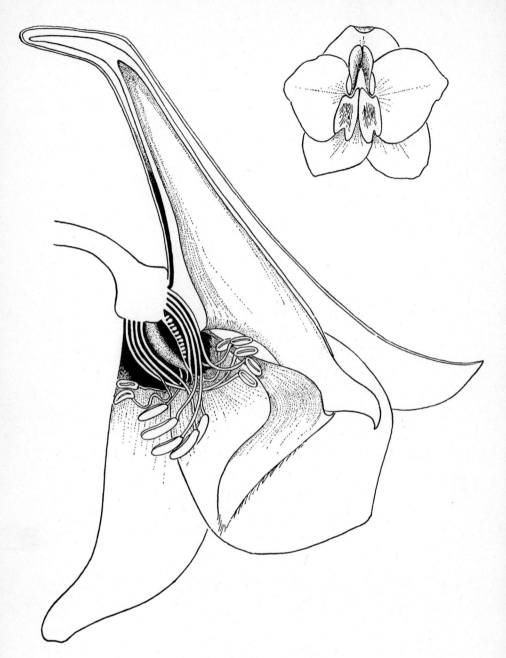

FIG. 31. Delphinium   ×6

DELPHINIUM, garden hybrid

RANUNCULACEAE

BLUE GARDEN DELPHINIUM

Inflorescence: a terminal and a few axillary racemes, often with a terminal flower; bracts 10–20 mm. long, narrow; flower-stalks 10–30 mm. long, lengthening after flowering; two bracteoles 10 mm. long, close beneath the flower.

Flower: hermaphrodite, zygomorphic.

CALYX: five spirally-arranged sepals about 25 mm. by 15 mm., deep blue-purple above, paler beneath, constituting the conspicuous part of the perianth. The sepal at the back has a long, wrinkled, purple spur, 15–20 mm. long, bent downwards at the tip.

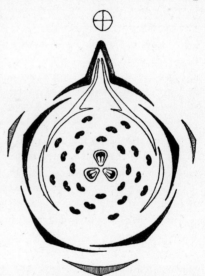

COROLLA: of four small petals, there being no front petal. The two back petals are in contact along their top edges, and are prolonged behind into spurs which lie closely side by side within the spur of the back sepal, reaching nearly to its tip. The spurs are independent structures only near their tips. For two-thirds of their length each is hemicylindrical but they are in contact by their edges so as to form a single cylinder. The two front petals

FIG. 30. Delphinium.

have narrow 'claws' or stalks, the grooved inner face of the claw being turned upwards to fit round the bottom edge of the corresponding back petal. Near the junction of the claw with the 'limb' or blade they touch and thus form the floor of a tunnel leading into the spurs of the back petals. The limbs of the front petals hang down from the entrance of the tunnel. Each has a central tuft of long, yellow hairs and is also hairy round the edge.

The colour of the petals is very variable. In some blue delphiniums they are a deeper blue than the sepals, sometimes nearly black; in others they are paler blue or white.

ANDROECIUM: hypogynous, of about twenty-five spirally-arranged

H

stamens. The filaments are about 8 mm. long, somewhat broadened and flattened below; the small purple anthers dehisce inwards.

GYNAECIUM: superior, of three carpels, 4 mm. long, slightly syncarpous at their base. Each bears two rows of ovules along the ventral suture. The styles are grooved on the inner side and end in stigmas shaped like horse-shoes.

NECTARY: the tips of the two petal-spurs secrete nectar.

Fruit: three follicles dehiscing along the ventral sutures, allowing the seeds to be shaken out.

Status: a perennial herb of hybrid origin, much grown for its showy blue flowers. The various parent species are not certainly known.

The Garden Delphinium is a good example of a highly specialized humble-bee flower. There is marked protandry, the stamens maturing in more or less regular succession from outside inwards. While they are shedding pollen they bend upwards so as to hold the anthers at the base of the tunnel formed by the petals, and therefore at the entrance of the petal-spurs. When all the pollen has been shed the filaments bend down and wither, and there is a steady succession of pollen-covered anthers at the entrance to the spur. When all have shed their pollen and bent down again the styles curve upwards and the stigmatic tips open where the anthers had been.

A bee visiting the flower alights on the front sepals and thrusts its head into the tunnel, extending its proboscis towards the nectar which collects in the spur. Meanwhile the anthers, or at a later stage the stigmas, are in contact with the lower side of its head, so that cross-pollination may be effected. Self-pollination is very unlikely to take place automatically, since receptive stigmas are held above the stamens, but it may occasionally occur during the visit of an insect.

A proboscis of about 13 mm. is required to reach nectar, and one of about 20 mm. to reach the bottom of the petal-spurs. Of the bees active during the time that Delphiniums are in flower only *Bombus hortorum* can reach the bottom of the spur, and this is by far the commonest visitor. The blue or blue-purple sepals attract the bees, while the pattern formed by the limbs of the petals and the yellow hairs on the front petals may act as honey-guides.

The diagrams show a plan of the corolla, and a longitudinal section of a flower at a fairly early stage. About half the stamens are immature and still curved downwards. Some have their dehiscing anthers held in the tunnel which leads to the spur, and a few have already curved down again and withered.

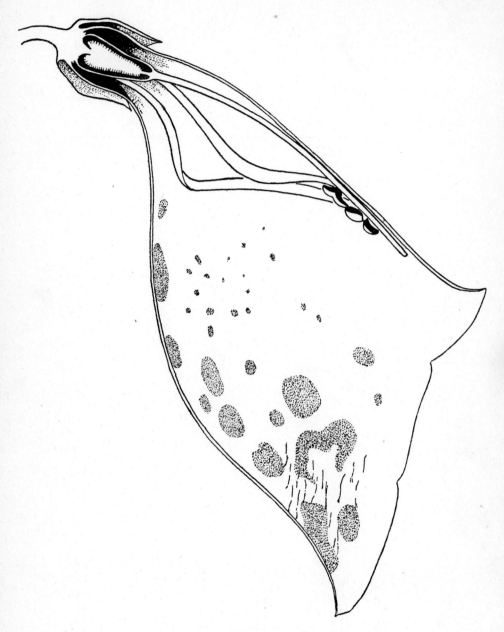

FIG. 33. *Digitalis purpurea* L.   ×4

DIGITALIS PURPUREA L.

SCROPHULARIACEAE

FOXGLOVE

Inflorescence: a tall, bracteate raceme, with flowers all directed to one side; 1–3 ft. high, lengthening considerably during flowering; from six to forty flowers may be open at the same time.

Flower: hermaphrodite, zygomorphic.

CALYX: five free sepals, with the back sepal lanceolate and much narrower than the other four, which are ovate.

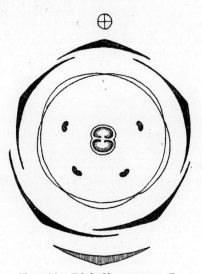

FIG. 32. *Digitalis purpurea* L.

COROLLA: sympetalous; tubular, 35–50 mm. long, widening at the mouth, the number of petal primordia being indicated only by the five-lobed margin of the long tube. The front lobe projects as a short, broad lip. The tube is purple-red outside and somewhat paler within, and along the bottom of its inner wall there are numerous dark purple spots centred in more or less confluent white circles.

ANDROECIUM: four stamens borne on the corolla-tube opposite the large sepals, the two at the front long, and the two at the back short. There is no stamen opposite the back sepal. All four stamens are closely pressed against the upper side of the corolla-tube, the filaments of the front pair being kneed to bring them into this position. The front pair are outside the back pair. Anther-lobes large, 3 by 1·5 mm., diverging from their basal point of attachment in a V at right angles to the filament, the point of the V directed towards the style.

GYNAECIUM: superior, syncarpous; ovary hairy, 10 mm. long, bilocular, with numerous ovules on axile placentae. Style bent, 20–30 mm. long, held against the upper side of the corolla-tube; two stigma lobes.

NECTARY: a yellowish-green fleshy ring round the base of the ovary.

Fruit: a capsule dehiscing along the partition between the loculi, the two valves separating from the axile column bearing the placentae. The small seeds are scattered a short distance by a strong wind.

Status: a native perennial herb of woods on an acid soil, flowering in June and July.

The Foxglove is a typical humble-bee flower, visited by large bees of the genus *Bombus*. The flowers hang obliquely downwards, and being closely crowded on the best-lighted side of the inflorescence present a large patch of purple-red. The projecting lower lip exposes some of the spots on the inside of the tube, and these, since they are visible as spots to the bee, may be regarded as constituting honey-guides, aiding the insect to recognize the flower. The flower is markedly protandrous, the two long front stamens dehiscing first, followed by the two short back stamens, the stigma-lobes meanwhile being closely pressed together and held against the upper side of the corolla-tube at about the level of the anthers of the long stamens. In the third stage the style has elongated somewhat and when the stigma-lobes diverge they are 3–4 mm. beyond the highest pair of anthers, and bend slightly downwards into the mouth of the tube. Nectar is collected in a depression on the under side of the base of the tube, and bees crawling into the flower to take it touch the stamens or stigmas with their backs. Protandry and the relative positions of stamens and stigmas make self-pollination less likely than cross-pollination, but in withdrawing from an old flower the bee may transfer the last remains of self-pollen to the mature stigma, so that self-pollination by insects is not excluded. In absence of insect visits pollen may drop from the anthers on to the mature stigmas, especially while the corolla is falling.

Humble-bees are the only effective pollinators, because of the width of the corolla-tube. Smaller insects occasionally visit the flowers and reach nectar by crawling up the corolla-tube but they often fail to touch the anthers or stigmas.

The diagram shows a flower in the staminate stage.

LAMIUM ALBUM L.

WHITE DEADNETTLE

LABIATAE

Inflorescence: opposite pairs of much-condensed cymes in the axils of leafy bracts at the top of the flowering shoot. The flower-stalks are very short and the ten to twenty flowers in the pair of inflorescences at one node appear at first sight to arise in a whorl. In the allied Catmints, *Nepeta*, the flower-stalks are much longer, and the inflorescences are evidently cymose, with a terminal flower and two lateral scorpioid cymes. Closer inspection of the White Deadnettle shows the same construction. Opposite each bract is the oldest flower of the axillary group, terminating the short primary axis. In the axils of its small linear bracteoles arise the two next oldest flowers, one to the right and one to the left. Subsequent branching is scorpioid, and the youngest flowers are furthest from the bract. The bracteoles lie as small linear teeth on the outside of the inflorescence in the axil of the bract.

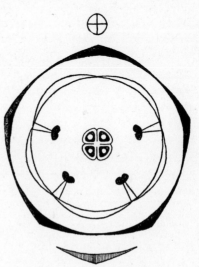

Fig. 34. *Lamium album* L.

Flower: hermaphrodite, zygomorphic.

CALYX: a narrow tube 4–5 mm. long, broadening above and prolonged into five long-pointed teeth, as long as the tube. The tube is ten-ribbed and pale green with a brown patch near the base on the anterior side. The tube and teeth are sparsely hairy.

COROLLA: white, tubular below and of four free lobes above. The tube is very narrow below and is almost closed by a fringe of hairs at about 3 mm. from its base, corresponding with an inward fold of the tube. Then it curves upwards, at the same time becoming inflated on the anterior side. It retains this increased diameter for 6–8 mm. and then opens abruptly to form the free lobes. These consist of a hood at the back, 8 mm. long by 3 mm. wide, strongly concave downwards; two short, broad, lateral lobes each with a minute apical tooth from the base of a notch; and a lip in front with two lobes which are curved downwards and have incurved edges.

ANDROECIUM: four stamens, opposite sepals, arising from the corolla tube, there being no back stamen. The filaments lie closely parallel beneath the hood, those of the front pair being longer, so that the anthers lie in two pairs, those of the back stamens below and behind those of the front stamens. The filaments of the back stamens are 7–9 mm., those of the front stamens 10–12 mm. long. The anther-lobes are 1·5 mm. long, black and hairy, the two lobes of one stamen held one behind the other.

GYNAECIUM: superior, syncarpous, initially bilocular but becoming quadrilocular by the development of a false septum. There is one ovule in each loculus. The style is attached basally in the centre of the ovary, is about 2 cm. long, and is held against the back of the corolla-tube and the under side of the hood. There are two stigma-lobes, about 1·5 mm. long, one prolonging the style, the other pointing downwards almost at right angles to it, and usually protruding between the anthers of the lowest pair of stamens, but occasionally between the two pairs of anthers. Each lobe is stigmatic only at its extreme tip.

NECTARY: two swellings on the front of the ovary base, extending more than half way round and to half the height of the ovary. During active secretion nectar collects in the narrow basal part of the corolla-tube.

Fruit: four nutlets.

Status: a native perennial herb of hedgerows and waste places, showing least vegetative activity in the summer, and flowering throughout the autumn and winter.

The White Deadnettle is pollinated by humble-bees with proboscises sufficiently long, at least 10 mm., to reach the nectar. The curve at the base of the corolla-tube causes the wider part of the tube to be held almost vertically with the hood curving forwards and sheltering the essential organs. The lateral lobes are directed forwards and the lip hangs obliquely downwards between them. The bee alights on the lip and grasps the lateral lobes. On reaching into the mouth of the corolla, into which it fits very closely, it first touches with its head the down-wardly directed stigma-lobe, and cross-pollination may thus be effected. It touches the anthers immediately afterwards, and pollen is shed on its back. There is no time interval in the maturation of parts, and self-pollination must frequently occur, both on withdrawal of the bee and automatically by shedding of pollen from the front anthers on the tip of the upper straight stigma-lobe.

The fringe of hairs near the base of the corolla-tube acts as a barrier to small insects which crawl down towards the nectar.

Humble-bees with proboscises too short to reach nectar in the usual way may pierce the corolla-tube, and honey-bees often take it through the holes thus made. Cross-pollination is of course not effected when nectar is 'stolen' in this way.

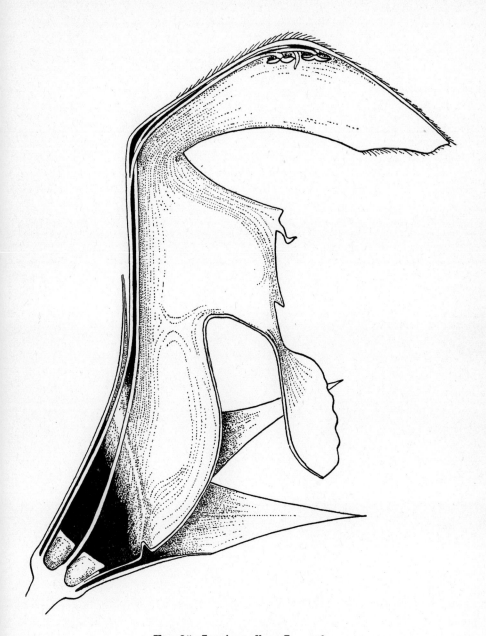

FIG. 35. *Lamium album* L. ×9

LUPINUS POLYPHYLLUS Lindl.

LEGUMINOSAE–PAPILIONATAE

LUPIN

Inflorescence: a terminal raceme up to 60 cm. high; bracts and bracteoles rudimentary or absent; flower-stalk short, 10–20 mm.

Flower: hermaphrodite, zygomorphic.

CALYX: pale green, softly hairy, gamosepalous, two-lipped nearly to its base; upper lip inflated, ending in two short teeth; lower lip acute, entire.

COROLLA: five free petals, blue-purple with darker veining. The arrangement and form of the petals are those characteristic of all the British members of the family Leguminosae and of the section Papilionatae to which they all belong. The section derives its name from the frequent resemblance of the corolla to a butterfly (Latin: *papilio*). A constant peculiarity is that there is a single petal at the back, not at the front as is more usual in flowers with five petals. This back petal, or 'standard', is the largest of the five, enclosing the others in bud. It is about 15 by 12 mm., rounded in shape. There is a groove down the under side, broadening in the basal half into a deep pocket. On the upper side this appears as a little fold becoming bigger and broader towards the base, where it fits into the inflated upper lip of the calyx. There is next a pair of petals, one on each side of the standard, called the 'wings'. They are about 15 mm. by 9 mm. and are concave inwards with their upper edges touching so as to enclose the remaining two petals which arise at the front of the flower. These stand vertically and adhere along their top and bottom edges to form the 'keel', enclosing the stamens and carpel. The keel has a sharp upwardly-directed beak with a small hole at its apex. There is also a slit along the basal two-thirds of the upper side of the keel, where the petals are not adherent. A fold near the base of each wing fits into a depression in the corresponding keel-petal, so that the two are interlocked. The four petals of the wings and keel have short stalks or claws about 3 mm. long.

ANDROECIUM: hypogynous or very slightly perigynous, of ten stamens in a single ring. Their filaments form at their base a tube 6–8 mm. long, but are free above, the free parts lengthening considerably during flowering. The anthers of the stamens opposite the sepals are large, 3–4 mm. long, of those opposite the petals small, 0·5–1 mm., the one opposite the standard being intermediate, 1 mm.

GYNAECIUM: superior, of one carpel; ovary flattened, hairy, 6–8 mm. long by 2 mm. broad, enclosed in the stamen-tube, with two rows of ovules on the upper side; style about 10 mm. long, bent from near its base so as to rise vertically at right angles to the axis of the ovary; stigma terminal, small, hemispherical, with stiff, erect hairs round its base.

NECTARY: none.

Fruit: a coarsely hairy legume.

Status: a perennial herb, native in Western U.S.A., cultivated for its long racemes of showy flowers which open in June.

The flowers of Lupin have a highly specialized pollination-mechanism. The anthers emerge in two sets. The first to shed their pollen, while the free parts of the filaments are still short, are those opposite the sepals. These have much larger anthers than the other stamens, and since their filaments remain short they remain throughout flowering in the wide lower part of the keel. The stamens opposite the petals dehisce next and their filaments, except that of the one opposite the standard, now elongate, the small anthers pushing sticky orange pollen from both sets into the apex of the keel. Meanwhile the short stamens are withering and the back stamen, opposite the standard, is shedding pollen behind the 'piston' formed by the other four anthers. The style elongates earlier than the filaments, carrying the stigma to the apex of the keel, where it is eventually surrounded by the anthers of the four long stamens.

In bud the standard is folded down over the wings and keel, and it erects soon after the dehiscence of the stamens opposite the sepals, whose anthers are then 1–2 mm. behind the stigma. Bees seeking pollen can now alight on the wings and in depressing them depress also the keel, because the two pairs of petals are interlocked near their base. Depression of the keel first causes the stigma to emerge through its apex. This strikes the under side of the insect and immediately afterwards there is an extrusion of bright orange pollen, especially in the later stages of flowering when the anthers of the long stamens have advanced to form the piston. The mechanism may be worked repeatedly, since the stigma returns within the keel when the insect departs, unless the flower is old. There is no nectar, so the flowers are visited only for their pollen. Only fairly heavy insects can depress the keel, and the most frequent successful visitors are the humble-bees, the colour of the corolla, blue or blue-purple, being typical of humble-bee flowers. Hive-bees can rarely work the mechanism, not being heavy enough.

Cross-pollination is favoured in early stages by the position of the stigma beyond the anthers, so that it strikes the under side of the insect

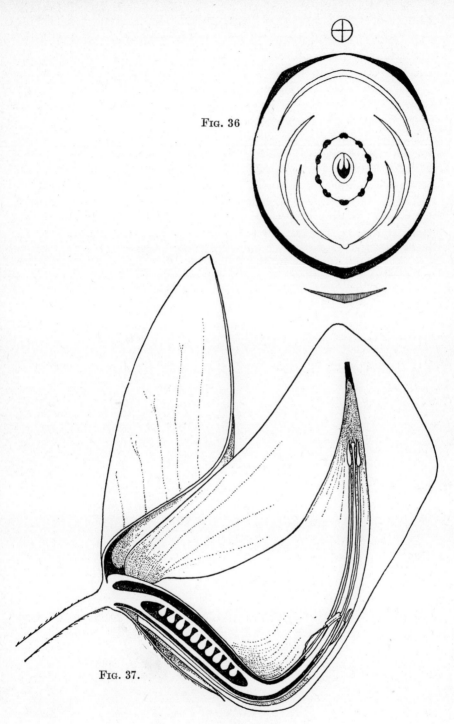

Fig. 36

Fig. 37.

Lupinus polyphyllus Lindl. ×9.

first. The hairs surrounding the base of the stigma make spontaneous self-pollination difficult, but it must often take place in later stages when the apex of the keel is filled with pollen. At this time, too, pollen is squeezed on to the under side of the insect before the stigma can emerge, so that when it does emerge it strikes a mass of its own pollen and self-pollination is effected.

The Lupin is an example of Hermann Müller's 'piston' type of Leguminous flower. It differs from Bird's Foot Trefoil, *Lotus*, Rest-Harrow, *Ononis*, and others in that the piston is formed from the anthers, not from a thickening of the filaments just behind the anthers.

The Lupin resembles other nectarless *Papilionatae* in having the filaments of all ten stamens concrescent at their base. It is interesting that the under side of the standard has a deep median groove flanked by the black dots and streaks which are called 'honey-guides'.

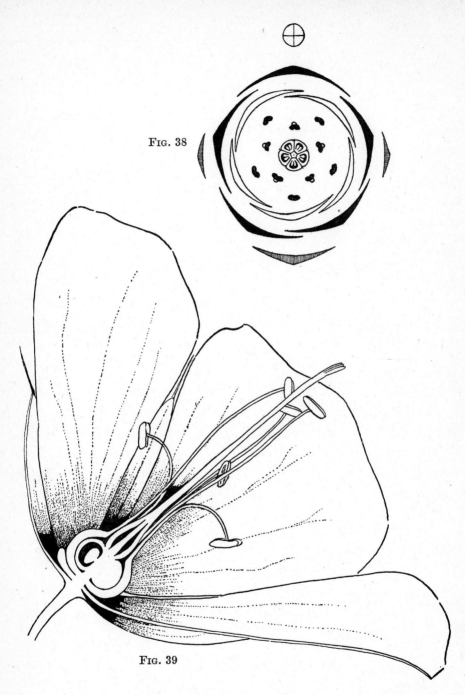

Fig. 38

Fig. 39

Geranium pratense L.   ×5

GERANIUM PRATENSE L.

GERANIACEAE

MEADOW CRANESBILL

Inflorescence: terminal and axillary cymes, at first dichasial but becoming monochasial and ending in pairs of flowers with stalks 10–20 mm. long.

Flower: hermaphrodite, actinomorphic.

CALYX: five free, spirally-arranged sepals, ovate, 11 mm. by 5 mm., green, three- to five-ribbed, with glandular hairs. Edges which are overlapped have a narrow transparent margin. Each sepal has a little spine-like point, 2 mm. long, at its tip.

COROLLA: five free, obovate petals, 18 by 12 mm., blue-purple with red-purple veining.

ANDROECIUM: hypogynous, of ten stamens arranged in two whorls, the five outer stamens opposite the petals and the five inner opposite the sepals; filaments lengthening to 10 mm. during flowering, with broad, flat, white bases, overlapping to form a cone round the ovary; anthers 2 by 1 mm., reddish-purple.

GYNAECIUM: superior, syncarpous; ovary 1·5 mm. high, strongly five-lobed with five loculi and two ovules per loculus on axile placentae. The loculi are prolonged upwards as narrow cavities in a beak 2 mm. long which tapers into the style. The single style lengthens to 8–10 mm. during flowering. It divides above into five slender, stigmatic lobes, about 2 mm. long.

NECTARY: nectar is secreted from five small, hairy glands between the inner stamens and the sepals, and collects as a single large drop in the base of each sepal.

Fruit: The persistent filaments and sepals stand erect round the ovary after the petals have fallen. The ovary enlarges considerably and the beak elongates to 25–40 mm. The tissues dry out and strains are set up which are eventually released by the sudden pulling of the loculi one by one from the axis. A strip of the beak attached to each loculus coils up like a watch-spring, dragging the loculus with it and flinging the single seed 3–6 feet away. The empty loculi are left hanging from the top of the beak.

Status: a native perennial herb of grassland and hedgerows, especially common on calcareous soils, flowering in July.

The beautiful blue flowers of Meadow Cranesbill remain open for three days, one member of each pair opening as the other fades. On the first day the inner stamens, those opposite the sepals, stand erect and their anthers dehisce. On the second day their filaments bend outwards and the anthers shrivel and fall off. Meanwhile the outer stamens, whose filaments curved outwards and downwards on the previous day, erect themselves in their turn and their anthers dehisce. On the third day the stigmatic lobes, until now tightly pressed together, diverge and form a five-rayed star with tips curved downwards. All or most of the stamens have lost their anthers, and their filaments have bent away from the style. There is thus very marked protandry, and self-pollination is almost completely excluded, since the stigmatic lobes are not receptive until they diverge on the third day, and then are held well above any anthers to which pollen might still be adhering.

The flowers are visited for their nectar by large numbers of short-tongued bees to whom the blue-purple corollas must be very conspicuous. The nectar is not freely exposed, but an insect with a tongue only about 1–2 mm. long can reach the drops which collect at the bases of the sepals. Besides bees, hover-flies may be occasional visitors. Cross-pollination takes place readily since first the stamens and later the stigmas stand in the centre of the corolla-cup and can hardly fail to be touched by a visiting bee.

It is interesting to compare Meadow Cranesbill with smaller-flowered species of *Geranium* such as *G. molle*, whose inconspicuous flowers are little visited by insects. Here, although there is protandry, the separation in time of maturation of stamens and stigmas is not complete, and the style does not elongate so as to carry the stigmas above the anthers. Consequently self-pollination is inevitable, the anthers shedding pollen freely on the stigma-lobes.

HELLEBORUS NIGER L.

RANUNCULACEAE

CHRISTMAS ROSE

Inflorescence: Either a single terminal flower, or a raceme with a terminal flower and a few lateral flowers in the axils of bracts; two bracteoles on the stalks of the lateral flowers.

Flower: hermaphrodite, actinomorphic, with elongated receptacle.

CALYX: five free sepals, arranged spirally, ovate, 40 by 30 mm., white or pinkish, green at the base.

COROLLA: about thirteen free, tubular, two-lipped, green 'nectaries' with outer lip (4 mm.) longer than inner (2 mm.).

ANDROECIUM: hypogynous, of about ninety free stamens arranged spirally.

GYNAECIUM: usually five free carpels inserted at the apex of the conical receptacle; ovary 10 mm. long, unilocular, with sixteen to twenty ovules arranged in two rows along the ventral suture; styles 5–8 mm. long, fairly stout, tapering, curved outwards, stigmatic at the extreme tip.

NECTARY: at the base of the cavity of the 'nectaries'.

Fruit: a group of five follicles above the persistent sepals which become green.

Status: a garden plant introduced from the forests of the Austrian and Italian Alps for the sake of its very early flowering.

The Christmas Rose is not a native of this country, where it is rarely visited by insects during its normal flowering period in early January, though early bees (*Apis, Bombus, Anthophora*) may be attracted by the large white sepals on warm February days. The flowers are protogynous and the stigmas often wither or are killed by frost before the stamens begin to dehisce. The styles, too, hold the stigmas well above the stamens, so that self-pollination is extremely improbable and the flowers normally do not seed.

The oldest or outermost stamens are the first to mature. During dehiscence they elongate and become erect, and then bend outwards and downwards until they lie horizontally along the sepals with their anthers directed upwards. The other stamens follow in order of age. A bee visiting the flower, standing on the sepals and thrusting its head towards the nectaries, thus receives pollen both from above and below and may transfer it to stigmas of a younger flower. The flower is not highly specialized, but only insects with a proboscis at least 2–3 mm. long can reach nectar easily, and only fairly large bees are likely to effect cross-pollination. It may therefore be called a bee-flower. Small bees, flies, and aphids occasionally come for nectar or pollen and may alight without touching the stigmas.

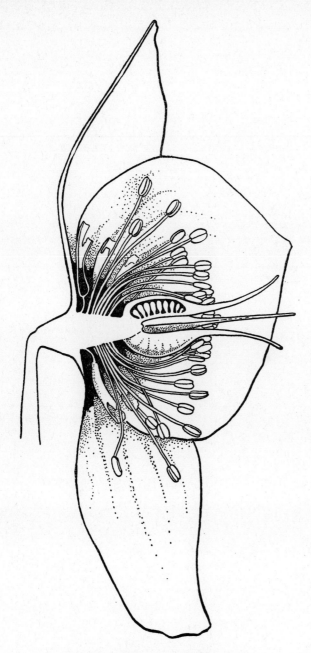

Fig. 40. *Helleborus niger* L.   ×3

LATHYRUS ODORATUS L.

LEGUMINOSAE–PAPILIONATAE

SWEET PEA

Inflorescence: few-flowered axillary racemes; bracts minute; flower-stalks short, 6–12 mm.; no bracteoles.

Flower: hermaphrodite, zygomorphic.

CALYX: green, hairy, gamosepalous below, forming a tube about 7 mm. long, and with five triangular teeth above, about 9 mm. long. The teeth end in long points, and their margins are curled back when the flower is open.

COROLLA: five free petals arranged much as in a Lupin, *Lupinus poly-phyllus* (Fig. 37), and other papilion-ate *Leguminosae*. The standard is rounded but rather broader than long, with a stiff claw enclosed in the calyx-tube. In bud it is folded down over the other petals, but un-folds so as to be concave downwards in the young open flower and con-cave upwards in the older flower. The wings are about half as large as the standard and are held with their upper edges pressed closely together forming a hood over the keel. Each has a short claw inside the calyx-tube and a groove at the base of the

FIG. 41. *Lathyrus odoratus* L.

limb which fits over a fold in the corresponding keel-petal. The keel-petals stand vertically and are concave inwards, adhering along their bottom edges and touching along their top edges to form a sheath round the stamens and carpel. They are clawed at the base, and are interlocked with the wings so that depression of the wings depresses the keel as well.

The colours and dimensions are extremely variable. The flowers of the wild species are reddish-purple in colour and are much smaller than those of the cultivated races.

ANDROECIUM: very slightly perigynous, of ten stamens arranged in a single whorl. The filaments of nine of the stamens, for the basal two-thirds of their length, form a tube 15–20 mm. long, with a narrow slit along the upper side. They are free above, and curved upwards. The remaining stamen, the one opposite the standard, has its filament free to the base and lies along the slit in the tube formed by the other nine. The anthers are small.

GYNAECIUM: superior, of one carpel; ovary hairy, flattened vertically, enclosed by the stamen-tube, unilocular, with two rows of ovules along the upper side. The style is curved upwards and flattened near its end where it is hairy on its edges and held vertically, at right angles to the ovary. The stigma is small, at the extreme tip of the style.

NECTARY: nectar is secreted from the back of the narrow perigynous zone and collects in the base of the stamen-tube.

Fruit: a hairy legume.

Status: an annual tendril-climber, native in S. Europe, cultivated for its handsome, sweet-scented flowers.

The Sweet Pea is a highly specialized bee-flower visited for nectar, with a mechanism quite different from those of Broom and Lupin, which are members of the same family but offer only pollen. The flower is large and showy, usually some shade of purple, and has a strong fragrance. The stigma is held beyond the anthers and pollen is shed on the flat part of the style, which acts as a kind of brush, retaining the pollen on its hairy edges. The insect, which must have a proboscis at least 15 mm. long, alights on the upper side of the wings and in depressing them depresses also the keel, since the two sets of petals are interlocked. Depression of the keel leads to exposure of the stamens and style and the bee inserts its proboscis along the slit in the stamen-tube under the back stamen. While it probes for nectar in the base of the stamen-tube its under side is struck first by the stigma, and cross-pollination may be effected, then by the hairy, flattened end of the style from which pollen is brushed. The chief visitors are species of *Anthidium* and *Megachile*, which are bees with abdominal brushes and long proboscises, and these can reach nectar and at the same time effect cross-pollination. The flowers of some of the largest cultivated strains are rarely visited by insects, apparently because of difficulty in depressing the large keel. They nevertheless set seed, so that self-pollination must take place spontaneously.

Towards the end of the summer the keels are often perforated by small bees, beetles, and other insects which steal pollen without touching the stigma.

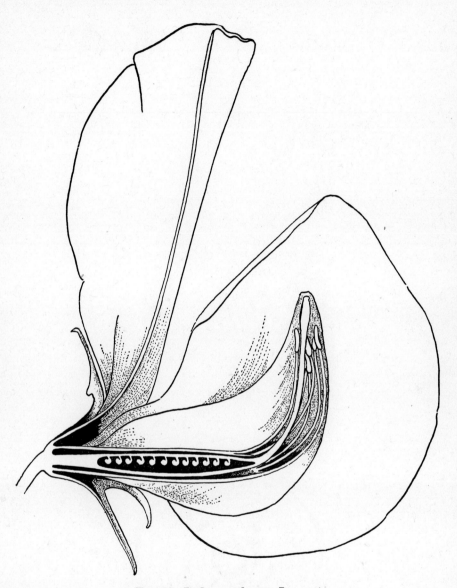

FIG. 42. *Lathyrus odoratus* L. ×4

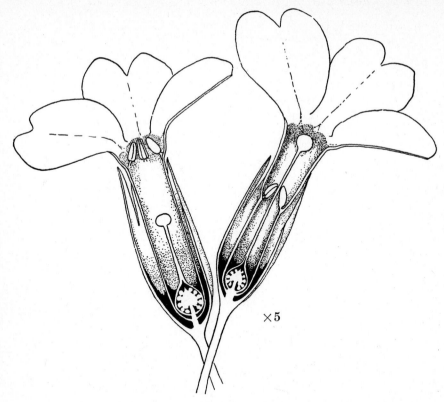

×5

Fig. 44

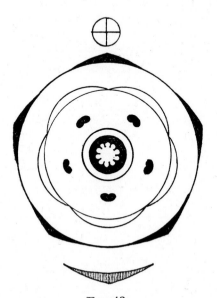

Fig. 43

Primula vulgaris Huds.

PRIMULA VULGARIS Huds.

PRIMULACEAE

PRIMROSE

Inflorescence: an umbel with the separate flower-stalks usually arising below ground from the common stalk. Occasionally the common stalk elongates sufficiently to raise the point of branching above ground-level. The flower-stalks are very variable in length.

Flowers: hermaphrodite, actinomorphic, of two kinds, differing in the relative positions of the anthers and stigma and in other points. All the flowers of any one plant are of the same kind.

CALYX: gamosepalous, pale green, forming a five-ribbed pleated tube below, about 10 mm. long and 5 mm. wide, and five narrow long-pointed teeth above, about 7 mm. long.

COROLLA: sympetalous, tubular below and with five horizontal lobes above, each ovate, 15 mm. by 12 mm., with a V-shaped notch at the end. The corolla is pale greenish-yellow except for an orange-yellow blotch at the base of each horizontal lobe.

The corolla-tube differs in form in the two kinds of flowers.

(a) PIN-EYED FLOWERS.

The basal part of the tube is pale cream in colour, about 8 mm. long and 1·5–2 mm. wide. There is an abrupt increase in width at the level of insertion of the stamens, and the upper part, pale yellow in colour, is about 7 mm. long and about 3 mm. wide, but widening from below upwards. The over-all length of the tube is thus 15–16 mm. At its top edge it is narrowed by a ring of thicker tissue.

(b) THRUM-EYED FLOWERS.

The tubes of the thrum-eyed flowers are somewhat longer, reaching 15–18 mm. The basal narrow part is about 14 mm. long, and the wider part, above the insertion of the stamens, only about 2·5 mm. long.

ANDROECIUM: five stamens borne on the corolla-tube opposite the corolla-lobes. The anthers are 2 mm. long and 1 mm. wide. In pin-eyed flowers they are unstalked and form a cone round the style at the base of the wider part of the tube. In thrum-eyed flowers they have short stalks, 0·5 mm. long, and form a cone in the entrance to the corolla-tube.

GYNAECIUM: superior, syncarpous; ovary globular, 1·5–2 mm. in diameter, unilocular, with very numerous ovules on a free central placenta whose narrowed end reaches the top of the ovary; style slender, ending in a round stigmatic head which stands in the entrance of the corolla-tube in pin-eyed flowers but at about 6 mm. from the top of the tube in thrum-eyed flowers, the styles being about 12·5 and 6·5 mm. long respectively.

NECTARY: nectar is secreted from the base of the ovary.

Fruit: a dry capsule dehiscing by five teeth.

Status: a native perennial herb of woods and hedgerows, flowering in April.

The Primrose is the most familiar example of heterostyly, that is, of a plant whose flowers are of two kinds differing in the length of their styles. The flowers with longer styles are called pin-eyed from the appearance of the style with its round stigmatic head, and those with short styles thrum-eyed. The anthers in one kind of flower are at the same level as the stigmas of the other kind. There is no difference in the time of maturation of anthers and stigma. Nectar collects at the bottom of the long corolla-tube and can be reached only by insects with a proboscis at least 12 mm. long. Such an insect, on visiting a pin-eyed flower, receives pollen on its proboscis at exactly the level from which it can be rubbed on the stigma of a thrum-eyed flower; pollen from a thrum-eyed flower can similarly be transferred to the stigma of a pin-eyed flower. Hence cross-pollination of pin-eyed and thrum-eyed flowers is readily effected if appropriate insects arrive. In April, when primroses are in flower, the commonest insect with a sufficiently long proboscis is the early bee *Anthophora pilipes*, and this is an active visitor and pollinator. The humble-bee, *Bombus hortorum*, can also reach nectar easily and is a frequent visitor. Certain other humble-bees, such as *Bombus silvarum* and *B. lapidarius*, can reach nectar if they thrust their heads into the wide part of the corolla-tube, in which case they touch the anthers of thrum-eyed and the stigmas of pin-eyed flowers with their heads, not with their proboscises. *Bombus terrestris*, with proboscis only about 8 mm. long, 'steals' nectar by biting through the corolla-tube just above the calyx. A few pollen-collecting bees visit thrum-eyed flowers, but do not effect pollination.

It is evident that in inserting or withdrawing their proboscises bees must frequently transfer pollen from anthers to stigma of the same flower or of the same kind of flower. In thrum-eyes flowers, too, pollen can fall from the anthers on to the stigmas. It was shown by Darwin in 1862 that in the closely related Cowslip, *Primula veris*, the stigma of the pin-eyed flower has much larger papillae than that of the thrum-eyed flower, while the pollen-grains of the pin-eyed are much larger than those of the thrum-eyed flower. In absence of insects the flowers set little seed, and the crossing of two thrum-eyed or two pin-eyed flowers gives a much smaller yield of seeds than when flowers of different kinds are crossed. The differences in size of stigmatic papillae and pollen-grains do not provide a complete explanation of these results. It has been shown more recently that the pin-eyed and thrum-eyed conditions are inherited as though a single Mendelian factor were involved, the thrum-eyed condition being dominant and most of the thrum-eyed flowers found wild being heterozygous. The prevalence of crosses between the two kinds of flowers, effected by insect visits, and the superior productivity of these 'legitimate' crosses maintain them in approximately equal numbers.

SAROTHAMNUS SCOPARIUS Wimm.

LEGUMINOSAE–PAPILIONATAE

BROOM

Inflorescence: flowers solitary or occasionally in pairs in the axils either of reduced leaves or of foliage leaves. Flower-stalk 10–30 mm. long with three minute bracteoles close together near the middle.

Flower: hermaphrodite, zygomorphic.

CALYX: gamosepalous below with a tube 3–4 mm. long, two-lipped above; lips yellowish-green, often with brown margins; upper lip with three teeth, lower with two teeth.

COROLLA: five free pale-yellow petals, arranged as in Lupin and Sweet Pea, with one at the back, the standard, and two pairs at the sides, the wings towards the back and the two which form the keel towards the front. The standard has a short claw and an almost circular limb about 15 mm. across. The limb is keeled above, and is at first convex upwards, but at the close of flowering it becomes concave upwards. The wings have a short slender claw and a narrowly ovate limb, 18 mm. by 11 mm. The limb has a large basal lobe on the side towards the back of the flower, and on the lobe a convex fold which fits into a hollow in the corresponding keel-petal. The wing-petals are concave inwards and are held vertically so as to enclose the keel completely in bud and partially in later stages. The keel-petals have a slender claw and a lobe like those of the wing-petals, the lobe folded to form a depression fitting the fold on the wing-petal, so that keel- and wing-petals interlock. The keel-petals adhere along their upper and lower edges, completely enclosing the stamens and carpel.

ANDROECIUM: hypogynous, of ten stamens, forming a tube below, 8 mm. long, but with free filaments above. All the stamens opposite the sepals and the one opposite the back petal have short filaments 5–6 mm. long; while the stamens opposite the remaining petals have long filaments, 16–20 mm. long. All the filaments are curved upwards except that of the stamen opposite the front sepal, which is straight and directed slightly downwards. This stamen, too, has the smallest anther.

GYNAECIUM: superior, of a single carpel; ovary 8 mm. long, flattened vertically, hairy at top and bottom, unilocular, with several ovules in two rows along the upper side; style 20–25 mm. long, hairy for the basal two-thirds of its length, slender, flattened at the end, curved upwards; stigma small, at tip of style.

NECTARY: none.

Fruit: a legume, dehiscing violently, the two valves curling spirally and flinging the seeds for some distance.

Status: a native shrub common on dry soils, flowering in May.

The flower of Broom offers only pollen to a visiting insect. The style is already longer than the filaments before the anthers begin to dehisce. The stamens opposite the sepals mature first and shed their pollen inside the keel. Later the stamens opposite the petals, including the four long stamens, dehisce, and at this stage insect-visits can be effective. An insect alighting on the wings weighs them down and with them the keel, since wings and keel are interlocked. If it is sufficiently heavy the keel-petals separate along their top edges, first the short stamens and later the long stamens and style being released explosively from the keel. Pollen which has collected inside the keel and on the flattened end of the style is flung over the insect, and still more is shaken from the anthers when they strike its body. The short stamens strike the under side of the insect, but the long stamens and style are more strongly curved and strike its back.

Many bees can cause the flowers to explode, the most frequent successful visitors being hive-bees, various humble-bees, and *Anthophora pilipes.* Hive-bees sometimes cause only the short stamens to emerge. Cross-pollination may be effected at the time of explosion, since the stigma strikes the bee's back slightly before the anthers reach it. It may also occur subsequently, since when the bee leaves the flower the style coils strongly so that the stigma is again directed upwards and the small bees and flies which glean pollen from exploded flowers are likely to brush pollen on it from another flower.

Self-pollination may occur during a visit, when pollen is flung all over the insect and the stigmas must receive some of it. The flowers do not explode spontaneously, however, and rarely set seed in the absence of insect visits. They are said by some authors to be self-sterile.

As in Lupin there are honey-guides on the standard—dark lines converging towards the centre of the flower—although no nectar is present. They may assist bees in learning to recognize the flower or to orientate themselves when they alight.

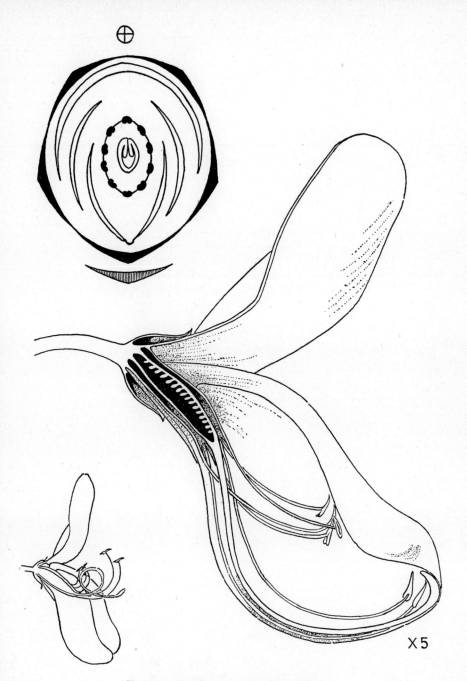

Fig. 45. *Sarothamnus scoparius* Wimm.

SCILLA NUTANS Sm.

ENGLISH BLUEBELL

LILIACEAE

Inflorescence: a raceme of six to forty shortly-stalked drooping flowers all turned towards the same side; bracts about 20 mm. long, narrowly triangular, deep purple in colour. The purple flower-stalk is about 8 mm. long, but lengthens during flowering. It bears at its base a single lateral bracteole, narrower than the bract and about two-thirds as long.

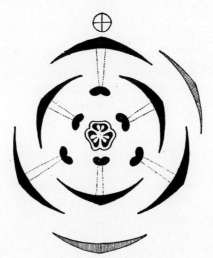

FIG. 46. *Scilla nutans* Sm.

Flower: hermaphrodite, actinomorphic.

PERIANTH: six segments in two alternating whorls of three, free except for the basal 1 mm., the members of the outer whorl partially overlapping those of the inner whorl to form a tube, about 15 mm. long and 5 mm. wide, which widens suddenly where the tips of the segments are curled back. Each segment is about 20 mm. long by 4 mm. wide, is purple-blue on the outside with a deep-blue midrib, and is paler blue on the inside. The outside of the inner segments is much paler where overlapped by outer segments than where freely exposed. No segment is accurately at the back of the flower, but one inner and one outer segment are lateral, the bracteole being opposite the inner lateral segment. The perianth is pleasantly but not strongly fragrant.

ANDROECIUM: six stamens borne one on each perianth-segment. Those on the outer perianth-segments are borne about 7 mm. from the base of the segment, and have filaments 8–10 mm. long, while those on the inner segments are borne only 3 mm. from the base and are slightly shorter so that the anthers of the longer stamens are held beyond and below those of the shorter, just within the end of the perianth-tube. The filaments are flattened and are pale blue in colour. The anthers, which are greenish-yellow, are about 4 mm. long and dehisce inwards.

GYNAECIUM: superior, syncarpous; ovary pale blue, 5–6 mm. long, broad below but narrowing above, trilocular, with numerous ovules on axile placentae in each loculus; style 5–8 mm. long with a terminal whitish three-lobed stigma which is at the level of the inner anthers when the flower first opens, but is later carried to or beyond the level of the outer anthers by further elongation of the style.

NECTARY: nectar is secreted from septal glands in the upper half of the ovary.

Fruit: a capsule dehiscing down the middle of each loculus to form three valves. The seeds are shaken out by wind but are not carried far from the parent plant.

Status: a native perennial herb especially abundant in oakwoods on a light soil; flowering in May.

Bluebells have been so named because each flower hangs obliquely downwards with its mouth towards the ground. It is chiefly visited by hive-bees, which grip with their legs the outwardly-turned tips of the perianth-segments while they thrust their heads into the tube in search of nectar. The flowers are slightly protogynous, so that cross-pollination may be effected at any stage. Since the stigma eventually reaches at least the level of the outer anthers self-pollen must frequently be shaken on it either by wind or during insect visits. Hive-bees, indeed, may often be seen probing for nectar from outside, passing their proboscises between the perianth segments at the level of the ovary. They do not touch the anthers and stigmas, and cannot effect cross-pollination, but probably cause selfing by shaking the flowers.

Lily of the Valley *Convallaria majalis*, Flowering Currant, *Ribes sanguineum*, and Harebell, *Campanula rotundifolia*, are other familiar examples of bell-flowers pollinated in the same manner as Bluebell.

The floral diagram is orientated in the conventional manner, with two perianth segments centred accurately in the median plane.

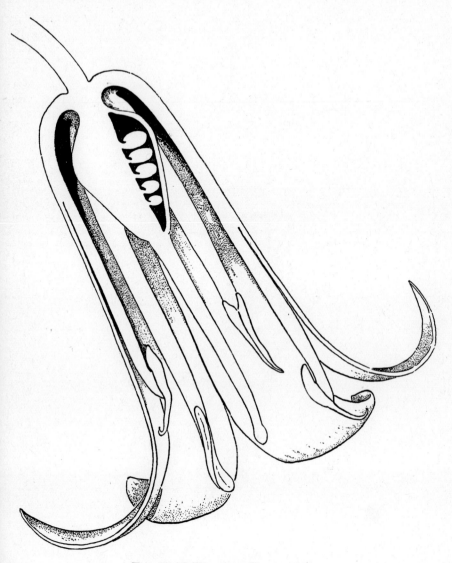

Fig. 47. *Scilla nutans* Sm.   ×10

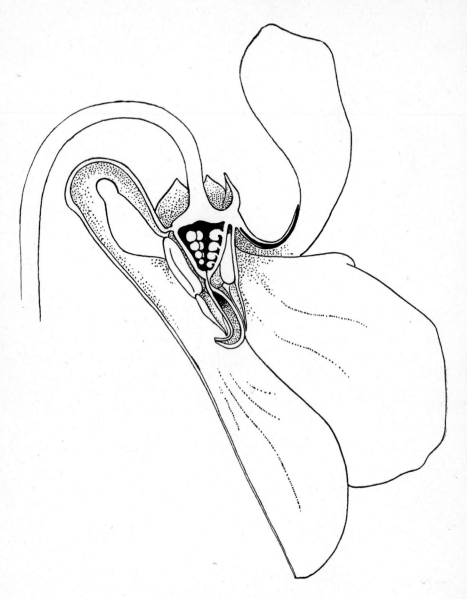

FIG. 49. *Viola odorata* L.   ×8

VIOLA ODORATA L.

VIOLACEAE

SWEET VIOLET

Inflorescence: solitary flowers in the axils of foliage leaves of the preceding season; flower-stalk 2–10 cm.; bracteoles close together, half-way up the flower-stalk.

Flower: hermaphrodite, zygomorphic.

CALYX: of five free sepals arranged spirally, green tinged with violet, ovate, with basal extensions 2 mm. long.

COROLLA: five free petals, all deep violet, paler at base; two at back 14 mm. by 6 mm., oval, with narrow claw, bent back when the flower is open; two side petals, 14 mm. by 6 mm., asymmetrical, with a small tuft of white hairs about 4 mm. from the base; and a front petal 14 mm. by 8 mm., slightly notched at the apex, and with a wide spur, 5 mm. long, compressed vertically and rounded at the end.

ANDROECIUM: hypogynous, of five free stamens alternating with the petals; filaments very short; anthers cream-coloured, 2 mm. by 1·5 mm., with a broadly triangular bright-orange connective tip, 2 mm. long; dehiscent inwards. The two front stamens have green, nectar-secreting appendages, 4 mm. long, which hang in the petal-spur.

FIG. 48. *Viola odorata* L.

GYNAECIUM: superior; ovary conical, 2 mm. long, syncarpous, unilocular, with three parietal placentae bearing about thirty ovules in two to three rows; style 2 mm. long, hollow, reaching beyond the connective flaps and bent at its end towards the front of the flower, so as to stand over the petal-spur; stigmatic surface at the narrow tip of the style.

NECTARY: the two stamen appendages secrete nectar, which collects in the petal-spur.

Fruit: a capsule, dehiscing by three slits between the placentae, and

L

opening in three valves; during drying the sides of the valves curl inwards, thus loosening the seeds, which fall to the ground.

Status: a perennial herb of banks and hedgerows, rare in Ireland, and extending northwards to Forfarshire; probably a native, but some consider it a relic of cultivation. It flowers from March to April.

The Sweet Violet has a flower so constructed that nectar is available only to insects with a proboscis at least 6 mm. long, and bees are by far the most frequent successful visitors, few other insects being active during its very early flowering period. The flower-stalk is curved so that the spur is directed obliquely upwards and the front petal becomes a convenient landing-stage. The pale bases of the petals and the dark veins which converge towards them make the entrance to the spur conspicuous as a dark hole fringed above with the hairs of the anterior-lateral petals. The style-hook projects forwards over the entrance, and bees attracted by colour and scent and alighting on the front petal must touch the stigmatic tip as they extend their proboscises into the spur, and cross-pollination may thus be effected. Pollen is shed between the anthers or through the apex of the cone formed by the connective flaps. Some falls to the floor of the entrance but much is shaken on the proboscis of the insect which touches the stigma. On withdrawal of the proboscis self-pollination may be effected, since in *Viola odorata* there is no stigmatic lip as in *V. tricolor*, where self-pollination is virtually impossible. The chief visitor is the hive-bee, *Apis mellifica*, but it reaches nectar with difficulty, its proboscis being only 5–6 mm. long. Humble-bees, *Bombus* spp., can more easily reach the base of the spur, but the most rapid worker is *Anthophora pilipes*, with a proboscis 21 mm. long.

Plants of Sweet Violet growing in a sunny situation may set seed in the ovaries of all their flowers, but the flowers are often half hidden by leaves on shady banks, and the scent from a small patch may not be sufficient to attract many insects. From about mid-May until September the plants bear numerous cleistogamous flowers which never open but nevertheless give rise to capsules with good seeds. Dissection of such a flower at the proper time shows the anthers lying against the ovary wall, and the style in a rudimentary condition, held beneath the connective flaps so that its tip is close to the anthers. Pollen-grains germinate inside the pollen-sacs, and the tubes pass through the ruptured apex of the sac on to the style, thence into the ovary, where some or all of the ovules, about ten in number, may be fertilized.

CENTAUREA CYANUS L.

COMPOSITAE–TUBULIFLORAE

CORNFLOWER, BLUEBOTTLE

Inflorescence: an involucrate capitulum, about 30 mm. in diameter; thirty to thirty-five florets, all tubular, differentiated into twelve outermost ray-florets, large and showy, and about twenty disk-florets, much smaller; receptacle a flat cone bearing the florets in depressions from the edges of which arise long, stout, white hairs, 6 mm. in length; involucre

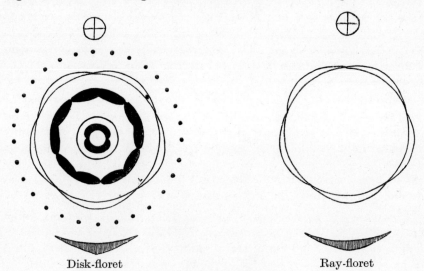

| Disk-floret | Ray-floret |

FIG. 50. *Centaurea Cyanus* L.

of about fifty spirally-arranged bracts closely overlapping and forming a flask-shaped structure widest near the base and tapering to a narrow mouth; bracts ovate-lanceolate to lanceolate, outermost 1 mm. long, and innermost narrowly lanceolate, 12 mm. long; greenish-white with broad dark-green midribs and scarious fringed margins.

Flowers:

(*a*) RAY-FLORETS: neuter, zygomorphic.

CALYX: absent.

COROLLA: sympetalous, forming a long tube 25–30 mm. long, very slender and white below (7 mm.), then bent outwards through almost a right angle, after which it widens rapidly into a blue, funnel-shaped mouth; the tube is entire for about 15 mm., then divides into a broad lip above and three or four teeth below. The upper lip is divided nearly half-way into four, sometimes five, long, pointed teeth, and is about

12 mm. long, the lower teeth being only about 3 mm. long, so that the flower is markedly zygomorphic.

ANDROECIUM: absent.

GYNAECIUM: absent; a minute epigynous zone beneath the corolla-tube contains no ovule.

(b) DISK-FLORETS: hermaphrodite, actinomorphic.

CALYX: represented by feathery hairs, about 2 mm. long, round the top of the inferior ovary.

COROLLA: sympetalous, of five petals forming a long, slender, white tube for the basal 6–7 mm., then widening, at the point of insertion of the filaments, for 2·5–3 mm., and ending in five linear-lanceolate, reddish-purple teeth 3–5 mm. long. The tube, especially of the innermost disk-florets, is bent through nearly 45° at the point of insertion of the filaments.

ANDROECIUM: five stamens borne on the corolla-tube and alternating with the corolla-teeth; filaments about 2 mm. long, white below, kneed inwards at about two-thirds of the way up from the base, with tufts of white hairs at the knee, pale purple beyond the knee. Anthers 5–6 mm. long, slender, cohering to form a dark-purple tube surrounding the style and surmounted by five small, triangular teeth. The anthers dehisce towards the inside of the tube.

GYNAECIUM: inferior; ovary flattened 2–2·5 mm. by 1·5 mm., unilocular, with a single basal ovule, surmounted by pappus and style; latter lengthening to about 15 mm. and dividing above into two short, blunt arms, stigmatic round the edge of the upper surface. Just beneath the stigma-lobes there is a ring of stiff hairs round the style.

NECTARY: a fleshy, yellow collar, 0·5 mm. high, round the base of the style.

Fruit: an inferior achene with a pappus of feathery hairs, wind-carried.

Status: a native annual herb, growing in cornfields, flowering in July. Much grown in gardens.

The disk-florets are strongly protandrous. The anthers dehisce before the flower opens and while the style is still below the anther-tube. As it passes up the tube, the stiff hairs beneath the style sweep the pollen before them into the top of the tube formed by the triangular teeth at the ends of the connectives. When the flower opens the style has reached nearly to the top of this tube and a little white pollen may be seen protruding from the slightly-curved tip. At this stage the filaments

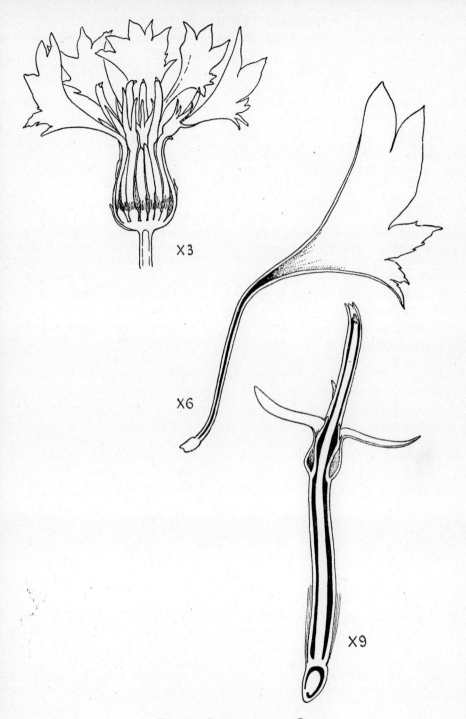

X3

X6

X9

Fig. 51. *Centaurea cyanus* L.

of the stamens are highly sensitive to contact, and if a visiting insect touches them with its legs, they contract suddenly, dragging the anther-tube down through a distance of 2–3 mm., pollen being extruded in a white thread which is brushed off by the under side of the insect. Contraction may continue for some time until the anther-tube has moved down through 5 or 6 mm., exposing the style, after which there is a slow recovery, and the process may be repeated with another insect. Meanwhile the style is elongating steadily and eventually emerges, the stigma-lobes beginning to diverge soon after they are clear of the anther-tube. An insect visiting at this stage touches the stigmas and may effect cross-pollination.

Self-pollination cannot occur spontaneously as in Dandelion because the stigmatic lobes are too short to curl back and touch the ring of hairs on the style. It may occasionally occur, however, when an insect visits immediately after divergence of the stigmatic lobes, while there are still many pollen-grains on the lower side of the lobes and on the hairs beneath them. When the insect withdraws it may easily brush pollen on to the stigmatic edges of the lobes.

The capitula are made conspicuous by the large, blue, funnel-shaped corollas of the ray-florets. Nectar is secreted at the bottom of a corolla-tube which is very narrow for 6–7 mm. at the base, then widens for 2·5–3 mm. Nectar rises in the tube and is accessible to insects with proboscises about 4 mm. long, if they thrust their heads down the wider part of the tube. The chief successful visitors are bees, especially hive-bees, long-tongued flies, and butterflies, bees being most abundant.

Cornflowers have tubular corollas in all their florets, in contrast with Dandelions, whose corollas are all strap-shaped. There is the further distinction that whereas the florets are all similar and hermaphrodite in Dandelion, in Cornflower they are differentiated into large neuter ray-florets and small hermaphrodite disk-florets, the former playing a large part in making the capitula conspicuous. Spontaneous self-pollination occurs in Dandelion but not in Cornflower.

CHRYSANTHEMUM CARINATUM L.

COMPOSITAE–TUBULIFLORAE

SUMMER OR ANNUAL CHRYSANTHEMUM

Inflorescence: an involucrate capitulum about 50 mm. in diameter when flowering; florets differentiated into about twenty ray-florets with strap-shaped corollas and 150–200 disk-florets with small tubular corollas. The ray-florets are variously coloured, the disk-florets always a dark reddish-brown. The receptacle is conical, about 7 mm. in

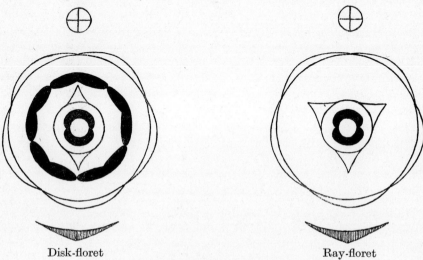

Disk-floret   Ray-floret

FIG. 52. *Chrysanthemum carinatum* L.

diameter. There are about thirty green, spirally-arranged, involucral bracts. The outermost are narrow and very strongly keeled, the keel being 2 mm. high and extending the whole length of the bract, which is therefore flattened laterally. The innermost bracts are broad and blunt with a scarious margin which broadens beyond the tip of the green central part of the bract, doubling its dimensions and making it almost triangular. Bracts also occur which are intermediate in form between the innermost and the outermost. Apart from the members of the involucre there are no bracts or scales on the receptacle.

Flowers:

(*a*) RAY-FLORETS: carpellary, zygomorphic.

CALYX: absent or represented by a few minute teeth.

COROLLA: sympetalous, with a short basal tube, 2–4 mm. long, and a strap-shaped blade, about 16 mm. by 10 mm., ending in three irregular lobes. The blade has two more or less distinct furrows running along its whole length from between the terminal lobes. The tube is vertical and is green and glandular-hairy, while the blade is held horizontally, directed outwards, and is variable in colour. It may be yellow throughout but is usually differently coloured at the base, frequent combinations being white with a yellow base, this with a red band above the yellow, and red with a yellow base.

ANDROECIUM: none.

GYNAECIUM: inferior, syncarpous; ovary 3–4 mm. long, triangular in section, with one side facing upwards, and slightly curved so that the corolla-tube is vertical although the ovary is inserted on the sloping side of the receptacle. The edges of the ovary are winged, the two edges of the upper side narrowly, and the lower edge with a triangular wing. The wings are thin, colourless, and transparent. The ovary is unilocular with a single basal ovule. The style projects just beyond the mouth of the corolla-tube, and divides above into two branches with broad, stigmatic bands along their edges and ending in tufts of long, reddish-purple, papillose hairs.

NECTARY: nectar is secreted from a two-lobed collar round the base of the style.

(b) DISK-FLORETS: actinomorphic, hermaphrodite.

CALYX: absent or represented by a few minute teeth.

COROLLA: sympetalous, forming a tube 3–5 mm. long, very slender below but widening abruptly at the level of the anthers. The separate petals are represented by five tiny teeth on the upper edge of the tube. The corolla is dark reddish-brown above and greenish-white below.

ANDROECIUM: five stamens borne on the corolla-tube and alternating with the corolla-teeth; the filaments are very short, and the anthers adhere laterally to form a tube, 1·2–2 mm. long, round the style.

GYNAECIUM: inferior, syncarpous; ovary unilocular, with one basal ovule. The ovary is 3–4 mm. high and is flattened with a broad wing on the inner and a narrow ring on the outer edge. The style and stigmas are as in the ray-florets.

NECTARY: a fleshy, two-lobed collar round the base of the style.

Fruit: a head of achenes with no pappus, shaken out when mature.

Status: an annual herb, native in Morocco, cultivated in gardens for its bright heads of flowers which open in July. Often called *C. Burridgeanum* in horticultural catalogues. Other species such as *C. coronarium* are also sold as Summer Chrysanthemum, but can readily be distinguished by the non-keeled involucral bracts.

The ray-florets mature first. They have no stamens but behave as carpellary flowers, and their style-arms diverge soon after the head opens. The stigmatic surfaces are receptive from the first and an insect alighting on the ray and probing for nectar cannot avoid touching them and may transfer pollen from disk-florets of another head.

The disk-florets mature next, the outermost first and those in the centre last. They are hermaphrodite and protandrous. Before they open, the tips of the five corolla-teeth appear white owing to reflection of light from their strongly-papillose outer surfaces. On opening, the dark reddish-brown inner side of the teeth becomes visible, and, in the centre of the floret, the top of the anther-tube. A little later pollen appears, gradually increasing in amount as it is pushed out of the anther-tube by the elongating style, the tufts of long hairs at the ends of the style-arms acting like a brush. The style follows in due course, the arms at first pressed together but diverging when clear of the anther-tube and exposing the stigmatic surfaces.

Insects are attracted by the bright colours of the ray-florets which make the head resemble a single large flower with numerous large petals. They often land on the ray and then crawl towards the centre, sucking nectar as they go. In this way they encounter first flowers whose stigmas are exposed, and may cross-pollinate them with pollen from another head. As they approach the centre they come to flowers in earlier stages with pollen-masses on the tops of the anther-tubes. From these they take pollen to other heads, or, if they crawl back to the ray, to flowers of the same head.

Nectar is secreted at the base of the corolla-tubes, about 3 mm. deep in ray-florets and 4 mm. deep in disk-florets. Since it rises almost to the top of the tube it can be reached by very short-tongued insects, and many different kinds are to be seen on the heads. The chief visitors are short-tongued bees, flies of many sorts, beetles, and butterflies, and any of these may effect cross-pollination.

Self-pollination may take place during the passage of the style through the top of the anther-tube if insects have not previously removed all the pollen, since the stigmatic surfaces extend sufficiently far round the edges of the style-arms for pollen to adhere even when the style-arms are closed.

Comparison with the Dandelion and Cornflower shows that the Summer Chrysanthemum represents a third type of composite flower. There is a differentiation of florets, as in Cornflower, but the outermost florets are strap-shaped and the inner florets tubular. The outermost florets, constituting the ray, are the conspicuous part of the head as in Cornflower, but are functionally carpellary instead of being neuter and sterile. Self-pollination can take place by a different mechanism from that found in Dandelion. It is interesting to notice that the strap-

M

shaped ray-florets of Chrysanthemum end in three teeth, but those which constitute the whole head in Dandelion end in five teeth. This is an almost constant difference between *Compositae* with some of their florets tubular and those with all florets strap-shaped.

The Ox-eye Daisy or Wild Marguerite, *Chrysanthemum leucanthemum*, closely resembles Summer Chrysanthemum in structure and pollination mechanism.

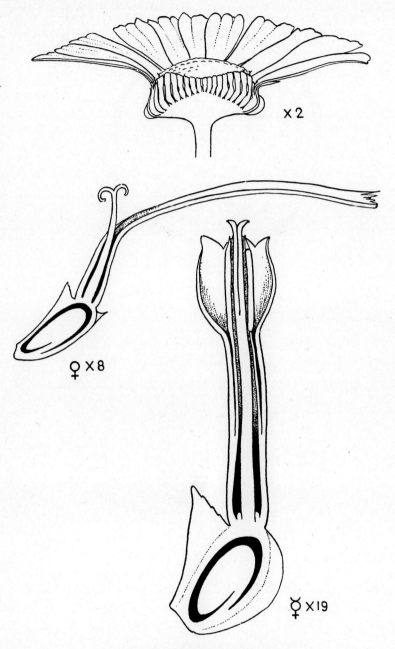

×2

♀×8

☿×19

FIG. 53. *Chrysanthemum carinatum* L.

FIG. 54. *Ranunculus acris* L.   ×7

RANUNCULUS ACRIS L.

RANUNCULACEAE

MEADOW BUTTERCUP

Inflorescence: a much-branched bracteate cyme, 30–60 cm. high.

Flower: hermaphrodite, actinomorphic.

CALYX: five free spirally-arranged sepals. The sepals are narrowly ovate and are hairy on the under side. They are green with a transparent yellow margin which is curled back, and there is often a dark purple-brown spot or line just beneath the tip.

COROLLA: five free petals. Each petal is broad, notched above, and narrowing below to a wedge-shaped base. The upper surface is glossy golden-yellow, opaque except for a translucent triangle near the base where the veining is more conspicuous. The lower surface is paler and not glossy.

ANDROECIUM: hypogynous, of forty to seventy stamens arranged spirally on the middle of the conical receptacle. The anthers dehisce towards the outside.

GYNAECIUM: superior, of about thirty free carpels borne spirally at the top of the receptacle. The flattened ovary is attached by a broad base and is unilocular, with a single basal ovule. It is surmounted by a very short style bearing a narrow, curved stigma.

NECTARY: there is a nectary at the base of each petal, covered by a small yellow scale attached only along its lower edge, so that nectar collects in a little pocket.

Fruit: a cluster of achenes, dropping when dry and mature.

Status: a native perennial herb of damp meadows and hilly pastures, flowering in May.

When the flower first opens all the stamens are curved inwards, completely concealing the carpels. Dehiscence begins first in the outer stamens, which stand erect and later bend back so as to lie on the petals, pollen meanwhile being shed from the slits on the outwardly-directed edges of the anther-lobes. Other stamens follow, the innermost dehiscing last. During this period short-tongued flies and bees can reach the nectary by crawling between the stamens which have shed most of their pollen and those which are still shedding it. Pollen is thus transferred to their backs, sides, and legs. The stigmas appear to be receptive from the first, but cross-pollination is unlikely to take place until a late stage, when most of the stamens have curved back and many of the oldest have withered and fallen. The path to the nectaries now lies between the remaining stamens and the carpels, and an insect may easily touch the stigmas with the side of its head and body. The movements of the stamens and their outward dehiscence combine to make cross-pollination rather more probable than self-pollination, but small insects crawling over the flowers in early stages must frequently effect self-pollination, and in many flowers the innermost anthers shed pollen while they are still in contact with the stigmas. In some localities the flowers are self-sterile, but this does not seem to be general.

The nectar is accessible to quite short-tongued insects, and the flowers are visited freely by flies and short-tongued bees, including hive-bees. Many of the visitors take pollen as well as nectar.

RUBUS IDAEUS L.

ROSACEAE

RASPBERRY

Inflorescence: few-flowered axillary cymes.

Flower: hermaphrodite, actinomorphic. The part of the receptacle bearing the carpels is conical, but a narrow perigynous zone, 2–3 mm. wide, forms a flange bearing the stamens, petals, and sepals on its outer edge.

CALYX: five spirally-arranged sepals, ovate, 10–15 mm. long, with a long apical point; they are pale green in colour and covered with short soft hairs, but with longer hairs along the slightly inrolled edges.

COROLLA : five free, ovate petals, whose edges do not meet. The petals are white and small, and stand erect or even slightly converging.

ANDROECIUM : perigynous, of about one hundred stamens arranged in four whorls; filaments white, stiff, those of the outer whorl broad and flat; anthers dehiscing along the sides.

GYNAECIUM: superior, of numerous free carpels arranged irregularly on the conical receptacle; ovary spherical, unilocular, with one ovule; style 4 mm. long, with terminal two-lobed stigma.

NECTARY : the perigynous zone secretes copiously and holds the nectar between the receptacle-cone and the bases of the stamens.

Fruit: a cluster of red drupelets, eaten by birds.

Status: a native perennial, much cultivated for its edible fruit.

The flowers are slightly protogynous, the stigmas being receptive when the flowers open, and the outermost, highest stamens beginning to dehisce soon after. Before the anthers dehisce the filaments are curved inwards over the carpels, but they straighten somewhat during dehiscence, their outer movement being restricted, however, by the erect petals. Whorls of stamens mature in succession from outside inwards.

Being neither very conspicuous nor very fragrant the flowers are visited rather infrequently. The inward curvature of the broad filaments makes nectar secreted by the perigynous zone accessible only to a proboscis 4–6 mm. long. The chief visitors are the longer-tongued bees, including hive-bees and humble-bees, and long-tongued hover-flies. When they alight in the centre of the flower they may transfer pollen from another flower to the stigmas, and in probing for nectar they inevitably receive pollen from dehiscing anthers. The innermost anthers dehisce while close to or touching the stigmas, so that self-pollination takes place in absence of insect visits.

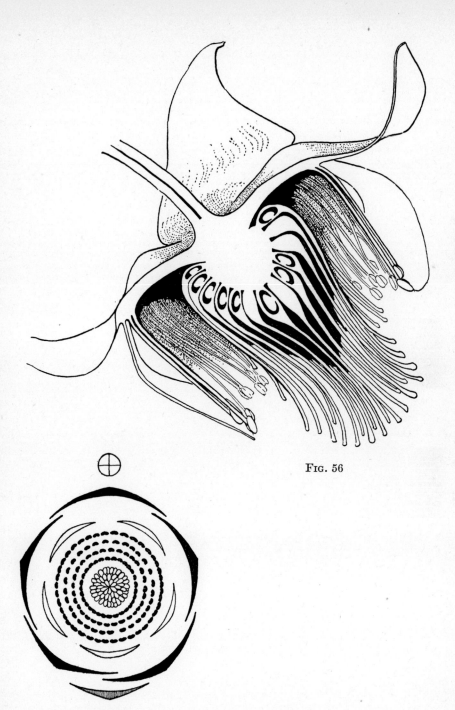

Fig. 56

Fig. 55

Rubus Idaeus L.   ×13

TARAXACUM OFFICINALE L.

COMPOSITAE–LIGULIFLORAE

DANDELION

Inflorescence: a capitulum of one to two hundred flowers, with an involucre of many narrowly triangular green bracts, arranged spirally. The outermost bracts, about twenty in number, curve back on the stalk when the capitulum opens. The remaining fifteen to twenty bracts are erect in their lower halves and then bend horizontally outwards beneath the outermost flowers. The capitulum is solitary on a long stiff, hollow, unbranched stalk which may bear a few bracts near the top.

Flowers: all similar, inserted on a flat receptacle about 6 mm. in diameter; all hermaphrodite and zygomorphic.

CALYX: a pappus of numerous soft white hairs, 4–6 mm. long, arising from the top of a narrow beak, 1–1·5 mm. long, which surmounts the inferior ovary.

COROLLA: sympetalous, forming below a hairy tube 4–7 mm. long and above a narrow oblong blade, 9–14 mm. long, ending in five small teeth. The tube is white and the blade bright yellow on its upper side but brown below, at least in the outer florets.

ANDROECIUM: five stamens borne on the corolla-tube near its base alternating with the primordia of the petals; filaments slender, free, up to 7 mm. long; anthers 3–5 mm. long, fused into a tube surrounding the style; dehiscence inwards into the anther-tube.

GYNAECIUM: inferior, syncarpous; ovary 1·5 mm. long, flattened, rough at its upper end with vertical rows of minute scales, unilocular, with a single basal ovule; style 10–16 mm. long, hairy above the anther-tube, terminating in two slender stigma-lobes, 1·5–2 mm. long, stigmatic over the whole upper surface.

NECTARY: nectar is secreted from a ring round the base of the style and collects in the corolla-tube.

Fruit: a head of inferior achenes each with a long beak and a pappus forming the familiar 'dandelion clock'. Dispersal by wind.

Status: a native perennial herb of grassland and waste places, flowering throughout the year with a maximum in May.

The *Compositae*, although the largest family of flowering Plants, including about a tenth of the total number, is nevertheless very uniform in its pollination-mechanism. There are variations in size and colour of the capitula, in accessibility of the nectar, and in the ease with which self-pollination can be effected in the absence of insect visits, but the essentials of the mechanism remain unchanged. The Dandelion is a good example of a relatively unspecialized member of the family, with all the flowers in a capitulum similar in form and behaviour.

The outermost flowers of the capitulum open first, and then flowers successively nearer the centre. They are protandrous, the anther shedding pollen into the anther-tube before the flower opens. When dehiscence of the anthers begins the style is short, the tips of the tightly-pressed stigma-lobes being at the base of the anther-tube. During dehiscence the style elongates and its hairs sweep pollen along the tube. When the flower opens the stigma-lobes are already emerging, and there is a yellow mass of pollen on the style beneath them. With further elongation of the style the stigma-lobes diverge, slightly at first, but progressively more until at the close of the flowering period they are curled downwards so as to come into contact with the hairs on the style.

Insects alighting on the capitulum touch the stigmas first and may then effect cross-pollination. In thrusting their heads down towards the nectar in the corolla-tube they remove pollen from the style of younger flowers, and carry it to stigmas of flowers on the same or different capitula. The capitula are very conspicuous through the massing of the bright-yellow corollas of one or two hundred flowers, and are visited by large numbers of insects. The corolla-tube is only about 5 mm. long and nectar rises in it almost to the top, so as to be accessible to very short-tongued insects. The chief visitors are bees of all sorts, long- and short-tongued, but flies and butterflies are also frequently to be seen probing for nectar. Cross-pollination must often be effected, but if it fails to take place self-pollination may occur in late stages of flowering when the stigma-lobes come in contact with the style and remove pollen-grains which are still retained by the stylar hairs. The combination of a simple mechanism for cross-pollination worked by a great variety of insects, and a means whereby self-pollination is made very probable in the later stages of flowering, is characteristic of many *Compositae*.

Dandelion flowers close at night and in dull weather. These movements are effected by the more rapid growth of the upper sides of the bracts and corolla-blades in a strong light and of the lower side in a weaker light.

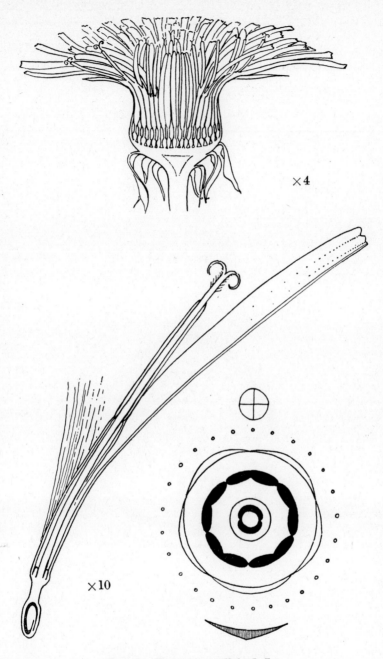

×4

×10

FIG. 57. *Taraxacum officinale* L.

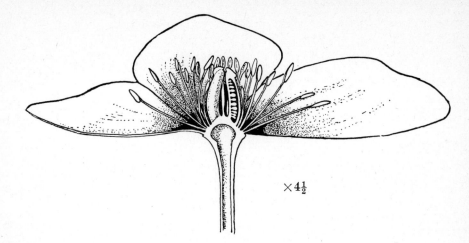

$\times 4\tfrac{1}{2}$

Fig. 59

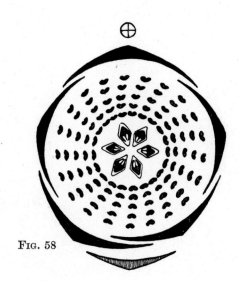

Fig. 58

Caltha palustris L.

CALTHA PALUSTRIS L.

RANUNCULACEAE

KINGCUP, MARSH MARIGOLD

Inflorescence: two or three few-flowered cymes in the axils of leafy bracts, of which the lower are stalked and the upper sessile.

Flower: hermaphrodite, actinomorphic.

CALYX: five, or occasionally six to eight, free, spirally-arranged sepals; broadly ovate, about 20 mm. by 16 mm., but graded in size, with the largest below; greenish-yellow on the under side, bright golden-yellow on the upper side.

ANDROECIUM: eighty or more hypogynous stamens arranged spirally: filaments 7–8 mm. long; anthers 2 mm. long, dehiscing towards the outside.

GYNAECIUM: superior, of five to fifteen free carpels; ovary 6 by 1·5–2 mm., tapering to a style about 2 mm. long with a small terminal stigma; ovules numerous, borne in two rows on the ventral suture.

NECTARY: nectar is secreted from two patches of glandular hairs on the carpels, one on each side of each carpel, about one-third of the way up from the base.

Fruit: a cluster of follicles dehiscing along the ventral sutures while still green and bending outwards to form a few-rayed star with the seeds exposed. The seeds are shaken out in winds which sway the fruit-stalk.

Status: a native perennial marsh herb, flowering in April.

The Marsh Marigold has no petals, the bright-yellow sepals performing the functions of both calyx and corolla by protecting the stamens and carpels in the bud and making the open flower conspicuous to insects. When the flower opens the outermost stamens have just begun to dehisce, and the stigmas are already receptive, so that there is no evident dichogamy. The stamens are at first curved inwards over the carpels, but as they dehisce they straighten, then curve outwards and finally lie horizontally on the sepals with their anthers turned upwards. The anthers dehisce outwards, so that an insect standing on the sepals receives pollen from above and below, as in Christmas Rose, *Helleborus niger*. The stamens mature in order of age, from outside inwards, and before dehiscence their inward curvature prevents an insect from touching the stigmas unless it alights directly on them. In older flowers, however, most of the stamens have curved outwards and the

N

stigmas are likely to be brushed by an insect visitor which may thus transfer pollen from another flower. While the stigmas are protected by numerous immature stamens self-pollination is improbable, but the last stamens to mature, the innermost, move away rather slowly and are still close to the stigmas when their anthers dehisce so that self-pollination can then easily take place with or without the aid of insects.

The large bright-yellow flowers are visited, chiefly for pollen, by early bees and hover-flies, hive-bees being the most frequent visitors. Nectar seems not to be secreted copiously except on warm and moist days. When it is present bees can be seen probing for the drops on the sides of the carpels, and on such days cross-pollination may be effected at any stage. When only pollen is being offered the insects are less likely to touch the stigmas until a late stage of flowering, after most of the stamens have dehisced.

German authors describe a very abundant supply of nectar, but this is not true for the neighbourhood of Oxford.

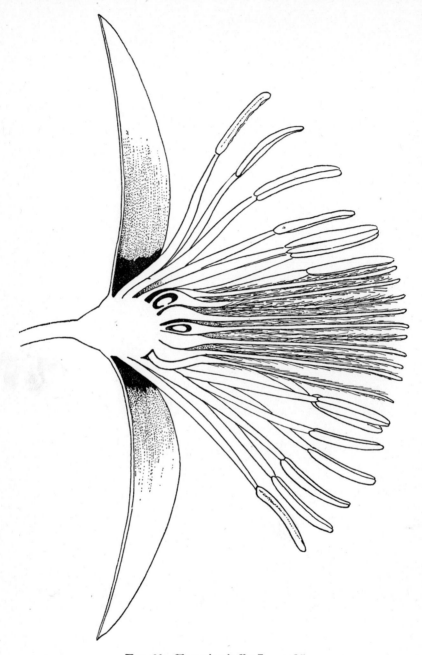

Fig. 60. *Clematis vitalba* L.   ×15

CLEMATIS VITALBA L.

RANUNCULACEAE

TRAVELLER'S JOY, OLD MAN'S BEARD

Inflorescence: opposite pairs of cymes, dichasial below and monochasial above, in the axils of foliage leaves, with small bracts and bracteoles.

Flower: hermaphrodite, actinomorphic.

CALYX: four or sometimes five free sepals, arranged spirally. When four are present they are often very unequally spaced. Sepals lanceolate, about 12 by 3–4 mm., but graded in width, the outermost being widest; covered on both sides with short soft hairs, and greenish-white in colour.

COROLLA: none.

ANDROECIUM: hypogynous, of about sixty spirally-arranged stamens; filaments 7–10 mm. long, flattened, greenish-white; anthers 2 mm. long, the same width as the filaments, dehiscing at the sides; outermost stamens often with rudimentary and sterile anthers.

GYNAECIUM: superior of fifteen to thirty-five free carpels arranged spirally; ovary rounded, very small, 0·5–1 mm., unilocular, with a single ovule, surmounted by a slender style, 6–9 mm. long, covered with white silky hairs; terminal 1 mm. of style stigmatic.

NECTARY: there is a slight secretion of nectar from the filaments of the stamens, on which it stands in small glistening droplets.

Fruit: a cluster of achenes. The ovary enlarges considerably during and after flowering, and the style lengthens to 25–30 mm. After the sepals and stamens have fallen the styles remain for a time closely pressed together in a cone, but later they diverge. When the fruits are mature they form an almost spherical head, the long styles with their silky white hairs being conspicuous objects in the hedgerows, and giving the plant its alternative name of Old Man's Beard. Dispersal for short distances by wind is aided by the feathery styles.

Status: a native perennial woody climber, common in hedgerows on calcareous soils, flowering in July and August.

The greenish-white flowers have a distinct sickly smell and are made fairly conspicuous by their numerous stamens and by massing. They are freely visited by short-tongued bees and flies which take pollen and lick nectar from the filaments of the stamens. There is no evident dichogamy, but the stigmatic style-tips are erect when the flower first opens, though soon bending outwards. The stamens, at first curved inwards over the carpels, straighten as they dehisce and then curve outwards and downwards. They dehisce in order of age from outside inwards. An insect alighting on the centre of the flower may transfer pollen from another flower to the stigmas. Self-pollination is unlikely in early stages because immature anthers surround the stigmas, but later, when younger stamens are dehiscing, becomes increasingly probable. In the final stages it may take place in absence of insect visits, since the anthers of the innermost stamens dehisce while still in contact with the stigmas.

THALICTRUM AQUILEGIFOLIUM L.

RANUNCULACEAE

PURPLE MEADOW RUE

Inflorescence: tall cymose panicles.

Flower: hermaphrodite, actinomorphic.

CALYX: five free, spirally-arranged sepals, small and green.

COROLLA: none.

ANDROECIUM: hypogynous, of about fifty spirally-arranged stamens with long, stiff, purple filaments, 6 mm. long, and small yellow anthers.

GYNAECIUM: superior, of about six free carpels; ovary 1·5 mm. long, with a long stalk, unilocular, with a single basal ovule; style short and thick with a stigmatic band along its sloping upper edge.

NECTARY: none.

Fruit: a cluster of stalked achenes.

Status: a tall perennial herb of alpine meadows in S. Central Europe, cultivated for its handsome panicles of crowded pale-purple flowers.

THALICTRUM MINUS L.

RANUNCULACEAE

LESSER MEADOW RUE

Inflorescence: cymose panicle.

Flower: hermaphrodite, actinomorphic.

CALYX: five free, spirally-arranged, green sepals.

COROLLA: none.

ANDROECIUM: hypogynous, of about twenty stamens with long, slender, flexible filaments and long, narrow anthers.

GYNAECIUM: superior, of about five free, unstalked carpels; ovary unilocular, with a single basal ovule. Style very short, stigmatic along its curved upper edge.

NECTARY: none.

Fruit: a group of achenes.

Status: a native perennial herb of dry grassland and sand-dunes, flowering in June and July.

These two Meadow Rues form an interesting pair somewhat comparable with the Lesser and Greater Plantains. The flowers of the Purple Meadow Rue, crowded into dense clusters conspicuous because of the numerous purple stamens, are much visited by insects seeking pollen, especially hover-flies and short-tongued bees. The stamens mature from outside inwards. There is no evident dichogamy, but in early stages of flowering the stigmas are hidden by the immature inner stamens, and visiting insects remove pollen without touching them. Later these stamens diverge and expose the stigmas, when cross-pollination may be effected by an insect alighting on the flower. Self-pollination easily takes place in absence of insects, however, since pollen from the anthers of the innermost stamens can drop on the stigmas.

The Lesser Meadow Rue has fewer stamens, which are pale yellow in colour so that the flowers are less conspicuous. Their filaments are slender and flexible, easily swayed by winds which shake powdery pollen from the anthers. The flowers being strongly protogynous, cross-pollination by wind may take place in early stages of flowering, and failing this self-pollination in later stages. The massed yellowish flowers are sufficiently conspicuous to be visited by a few insects which again may effect either cross- or self-pollination. The Lesser Meadow Rue may be compared with Lesser Plantain, *Plantago media*, in that both are pollinated sometimes by wind and sometimes by insects. The Meadow Rue, however, is pollinated predominantly by wind, the Plantain predominantly by insects. They are interesting in being intermediate between the highly specialized types which are pollinated exclusively in one or the other way.

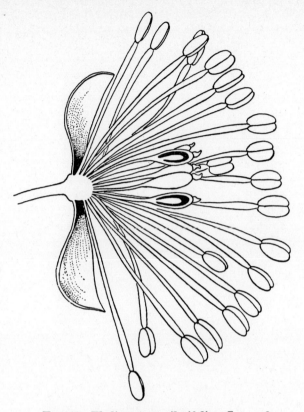

FIG. 61. *Thalictrum aquilegifolium* L. ×8

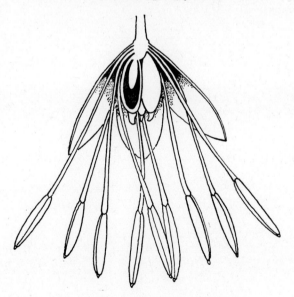

FIG. 62. *Thalictrum minus* L. ×15

SCROPHULARIA AQUATICA L.

SCROPHULARIACEAE

FIGWORT

Inflorescence: terminal and axillary panicles up to 60 cm. high; race-mose with almost opposite lateral pairs of cymes, dichasial in their first branching, then monochasial; bracts narrow, 10–20 mm. long near the base of the inflorescence, but becoming minute near the apex.

Flower: hermaphrodite, zygomorphic.

CALYX: gamosepalous below (2 mm.), divided above into five more or less equal rounded lobes 2–3 mm. long, green, with narrow scarious margins.

COROLLA: sympetalous below, forming a short, wide tube 3–4 mm. by 3 mm., divided above into five erect segments, two back segments forming a rounded upper lip about 3 mm. long by 4 mm. wide, two-lobed to half its length, the two halves overlapping; two at the sides and towards the front 1 mm. long by 2–3 mm. wide, and one at the front 1–1·5 mm. long by 2 mm. wide, becoming curled downwards during flowering; back of tube and back segments reddish-brown; rest of corolla pale greenish-red.

ANDROECIUM: four functional stamens and one small petal-like stami-node at the back, inserted at the base of the corolla-tube, and alternating with the corolla-segments; filaments 3–5 mm., stout, glandular hairy; those of the front stamens straight, those of the back curved near their base towards the lower (front) side of the flower; all four have filaments strongly curled so that the anthers are held close to the base of the corolla-tube in the early stage of flowering; anthers, borne on the some-what swollen end of the filaments, elongate at right angles to the axis of the filament and in the transverse plane of the flower, dehiscing by a single horizontal slit along the top; staminode a small (1 mm.) petal-like lobe lying between the two back corolla-lobes, and inserted at their base.

GYNAECIUM: superior, syncarpous; ovary with two loculi, each with numerous ovules on axile placentae; style slender, 3 mm. long, curved forward at its tip; stigma small, terminal, two-lobed, covered with long papillae.

NECTARY: a fleshy yellow ring round the base of the ovary.

Fruit: a capsule dehiscing along the partition wall between the two loculi.

Status: a native perennial herb growing on the banks of streams and ditches, flowering in July.

The Figworts are amongst the few members of our flora which are normally pollinated by wasps. The flowers are strongly protogynous. In the first stage the style is curved forward over the front corolla-lobe, which is curled down at the tip, the stigma being held about 5 mm. beyond this lobe. The anthers are meanwhile held near the base of the corolla-tube by their strongly curled filaments. On sunny days wasps visit the flowers freely for nectar, which collects at the base of the short wide corolla-tube. In the first stage of flowering a wasp grasping the corolla-lobes with its legs touches the stigma with the under side of its head or body, and may effect cross-pollination. If this takes place the stigma withers and the four anthers appear at the front of the corolla-tube, just behind the stigma. Dehiscence has already begun when they reach their final position, and visiting wasps now receive pollen which may be transferred to another flower.

In the absence of pollination in the first stage the stigma does not wither but remains receptive while the anthers dehisce, and is then practically certain to receive self-pollen either by the agency of a wasp, or through grains falling from the anthers. Self-pollination seems to take place regularly in cold and sunless weather when few wasps are flying. The allied species *S. nodosa*, which flowers much earlier (in June), can rarely have its first flowers visited by wasps, yet it seeds freely. Here the flowers are usually self-pollinated, only those opening latest having much chance of visits from wasps.

Hermann Müller records a few visits by bees, *Bombus agrorum*, and species of *Halictus*, but these are very small in number compared with those by wasps.

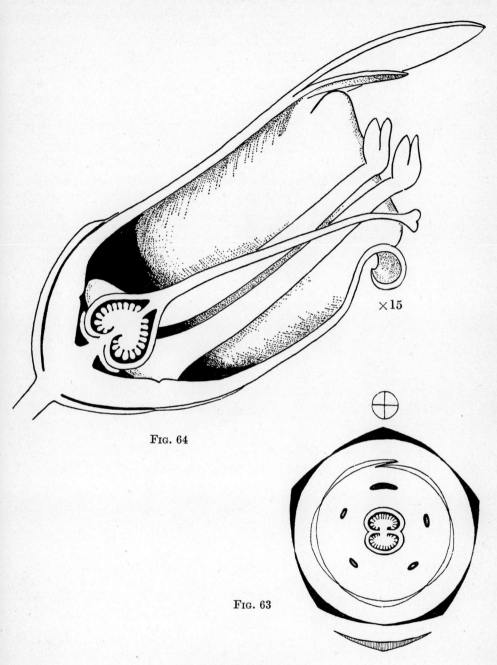

FIG. 64

×15

FIG. 63

Scrophularia aquatica L.

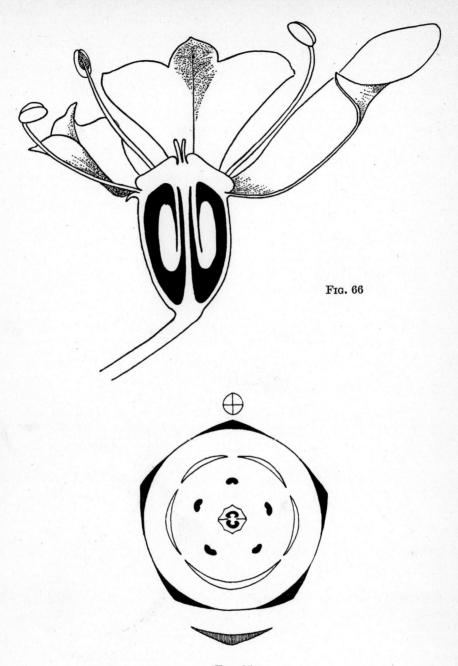

Fig. 66

Fig. 65

Heracleum Sphondylium L.

HERACLEUM SPHONDYLIUM L.

UMBELLIFERAE

HOGWEED

Inflorescence: a compound umbel 15–20 cm. across, the small flowers being closely aggregated in the partial umbels which are themselves held fairly closely together; general involucre absent or of one narrow bract; partial involucres of six to twelve narrow bracts; stalks of partial umbels 25–75 mm., of flowers 8–18 mm.

Flower: hermaphrodite or staminate, actinomorphic or zygomorphic according to position in the partial umbel.

CALYX: five minute teeth above the hairy inferior ovary.

COROLLA: five free ovate-acute white petals, slightly concave with incurved apex; central flowers of partial umbels actinomorphic; marginal flowers zygomorphic, with their three outermost petals large and deeply two-lobed, with incurved tips; the middle petal of the three symmetrically two-lobed, the two lateral petals asymmetrically two-lobed, their large lobes being those nearer the margin of the partial umbel.

ANDROECIUM: epigynous, of five stamens alternating with the petals; anthers small, round, dehiscing by lateral slits.

GYNAECIUM: inferior, syncarpous, bilocular, with a single, pendulous ovule in each loculus; styles two, 4–5 mm. long, each terminating in a small semicircular stigmatic area which slopes inwards. Some of the central flowers of each partial umbel may be staminate only and therefore sterile.

NECTARY: nectar is secreted from the massive conical disk at the base of the styles above the insertion of the stamens. This is pale green in colour, and is deeply grooved in the plane of the ovary. The nectar stands in small glistening droplets.

Fruit: splitting into two dry, one-seeded, indehiscent halves, each flattened, with a narrow marginal wing; dispersal by wind.

Status: a native growing in hedgerows and hilly pastures, and flowering in summer with a maximum in July.

The flowers of Hogweed are typical of the family *Umbelliferae*. They are small and white and individually inconspicuous but are massed in large flat-topped inflorescences made more conspicuous by the zygomorphic corollas of the marginal flowers. They have a distinct sickly smell and secrete nectar copiously. The nectar is freely exposed in drops

O

on the top of the inferior ovary so that it can be taken even by the shortest-tongued insects. Perhaps no flower has a greater number of different insect visitors.

Before the flowers open the essential organs are enclosed by the inrolled petals, and when these straighten they expose the stamens with their filaments strongly coiled inwards so that the anthers are held near the base of the petals. The filaments soon uncoil, become erect, and later lie in a horizontal plane with the ends turned slightly upwards, the anthers meanwhile dehiscing. The flowers are strongly protandrous, the styles at first being very short, less than $\frac{1}{2}$ mm., and pressed tightly together. The filaments continue their outward movement until, when all the pollen has been shed, they are curved back below the plane of the petals with the anthers directed upwards, and they fall soon afterwards. The styles grow rapidly during the early stages of flowering but do not diverge to expose the stigmas until after the stamens have fallen.

The visiting insects are small flies, beetles, wasps, and short-tongued bees which crawl over the inflorescence, taking the freely accessible nectar and becoming covered with pollen which they transfer to flowers whose stigmas are mature. Secretion of nectar and visits by insects continue after the petals have fallen. Self-pollination is almost excluded by the pronounced protandry.

The diagram (Fig.66) shows a marginal flower in the staminate stage.

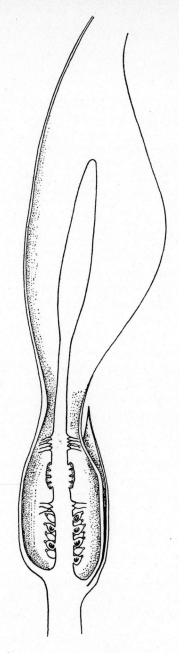

FIG. 67. *Arum maculatum* L. $\times \frac{3}{2}$

ARUM MACULATUM L.

AROIDEAE (ARACEAE)

CUCKOO PINT, WILD ARUM, LORDS AND LADIES

Inflorescence: the flowers are unstalked and are borne tightly pressed together on the fleshy axis ('spadix') which terminates the annual leafy shoot. The end of the axis is club-shaped and bare of flowers for a distance of 5–6 cm. It projects as a dull purple club from the large pale-green sheathing bract ('spathe'), 8–10 mm. long, whose cylindrical base encloses the flower-bearing part of the axis. The basal chamber formed by the spathe is about 35 mm. long by 20 mm. wide, and is narrowed at the mouth, where it is only 10–13 mm. wide.

Flowers: the flowers are of four kinds, arranged in order on the spadix.

At the bottom of the inflorescence are thirty to fifty carpellary flowers, arranged irregularly. There are no bracts or bracteoles and each flower consists only of a pale-yellow ovary, 3 mm. high, syncarpous, unilocular, with two rows of two to three ovules on its upper wall; style very short; stigma unlobed.

Above the carpellary flowers are eight to fifteen sterile flowers with swollen bases and terminal filamentous processes up to 5 mm. long. These may be termed non-functional carpellary flowers.

Next follows a zone of about one hundred almost stalkless anthers 1 mm. long, arranged more or less in pairs. It is usually supposed that these are staminate flowers each consisting of two stamens, with no bracts, bracteoles, or perianth. Dehiscence is by two longitudinal slits, and the pollen is yellow.

The top zone consists of thirty to forty functionless flowers which are small cones of undifferentiated tissue with long terminal filaments 4–5 mm. long. The filamentous processes reach the inner wall of the spathe just beneath the entrance to the basal chamber.

NECTARY: none.

Fruit: a cluster of scarlet berries, readily eaten by birds.

Status: a native perennial herb of shady hedgerows and woods, flowering in April and May.

The inflorescence of the Cuckoo Pint is comparable with those of Summer Chrysanthemum, Dandelion, and Cornflower in that it functions as a single insect-attracting unit. It differs from these in the greater differentiation of its flowers and in constituting what may be termed a 'trap-mechanism'.

The inflorescence gives off an unpleasant sickly smell from the time it first opens, and flies, especially quite small flies of the genus *Psychoda*, are attracted by it and perhaps also by the dull purple club-like end of the spadix. This combination of a somewhat fetid smell with a dull reddish or purplish colour is very characteristic of flowers pollinated by certain flies. A third feature which may assist in attracting flies is the remarkable rise in temperature of the spadix-tip. This accompanies the disappearance of large quantities of starch and a very high rate of respiration. It is suggested that small flies may be led to enter the spathe for shelter in the somewhat warmer air found within it. Church finds that the temperature of the spadix rises 10–12° C. above that of the surrounding air, and that this may cause the air in the basal chamber to be 1–3° C. above outside air-temperature.

Flies crawling down the surface of the spathe enter the chamber past the filamentous processes of the uppermost flowers, and are then trapped in so far as they cannot easily fly out into the open air although they can, of course, crawl back along the path by which they entered. Many die, possibly owing to an accumulation of carbon dioxide from the rapidly respiring spadix. The stigmas are receptive during the first day after opening, but the anthers do not dehisce until the second or even third day, and when they wither the guard filaments also droop and any surviving flies are released, covered with pollen, to visit another inflorescence. The inflorescence thus functions as a protogynous flower, though this term cannot strictly be applied to it since we are not dealing with a single hermaphrodite flower. It should be noted that the relative position of the staminate and carpellary flowers would give earlier maturation of the latter apart from any secondary adjustments.

Flies are trapped in considerable numbers, as can easily be observed, and the carpellary flowers are freely pollinated, so that large clusters of berries are formed.

ARRHENATHERUM ELATIUS Mert. and Koch.

(*H. AVENACEUM* Beav.)

GRAMINEAE

TALL, OR FALSE, OAT GRASS

Inflorescence: a panicle of spikelets up to 30 cm. high, with numerous whorls of branches, there being three or four branches in a whorl. The branches are horizontal during flowering but later are held vertically close to the main axis of the panicle. Each spikelet has two flowers, back to back, the lower staminate and the upper hermaphrodite, and is enclosed within two empty glumes. The lower empty glume is narrow and one-veined, less than half as long as the spikelet. The upper is broader, three-veined, and almost as long as the spikelet. The spikelet stands horizontal while flowering.

Flowers:

(*a*) HERMAPHRODITE FLOWER.

LOWER FLOWERING GLUME almost enclosed by the upper empty glume. It is about 8 mm. long, ovate, pointed, strongly concave, faintly six-veined, with an awn 5–6 mm. long inserted on the back about 2 mm. behind the tip.

UPPER FLOWERING GLUME as long as the lower; narrow, pointed, two-veined, with inrolled margins.

LODICULES: two narrow long-pointed scales with swollen bases, one each side of the front of the ovary.

ANDROECIUM: hypogynous, of three stamens with filaments 11 mm. long and very slender, suspending the long narrow anthers in a vertical position below the spikelet. The anthers are reddish-purple in colour.

GYNAECIUM: superior, syncarpous; ovary rounded, unilocular, with one ovule attached near the base at the back. Two short styles hold long feathery stigmas, 3–4 mm. long, horizontally between the flowering glumes of open flowers.

NECTARY: none.

Fruit: an achene with seed-wall adhering to the ovary-wall, enclosed in the flowering glumes, the awn of the lower flowering glume elongating and becoming twisted.

(*b*) STAMINATE FLOWER.

The staminate flower is similar to the hermaphrodite flower in most respects. The chief differences are that the awn of the lower flowering glume is inserted half-way along the back of the glume and is 12–20 mm.

long, becoming kneed and twisted after flowering; and that the ovary
is rudimentary, with a tiny stigma-like process at its apex.

Status: a tall native perennial grass of pastures and hedgerows, flowering in June.

All grasses are wind-pollinated and have features in common, some
of which can be related to their mode of pollination. They have no
brightly-coloured perianth, no nectary, and no scent. Their flowers are
typically grouped in spikelets consisting of a short axis bearing two
membranous scales at its base. These are the empty glumes. Higher on
the axis are other somewhat similar scales, the lower flowering glumes, and
since each bears a flower in its axil, they may be interpreted as bracts.
The flower has an axis bearing first, opposite the lower flowering glume,
a very delicate scale called the palea, or upper flowering glume, often
interpreted as a bracteole. Above this towards the front of the flower,
that is towards the side where the bract is, are two tiny scales called
lodicules. These are believed by some botanists to be vestiges of a
perianth. Next come three stamens, one at the front and two at the
back and finally an ovary, unilocular with a single ovule, bearing two
feathery stigmas. The spikelets are aggregated into spikes and panicles
behaving like individual flowers of other plants.

In Tall Oat Grass the spikelets are in panicles and each has only two
flowers, one hermaphrodite, the other staminate. The two stand back
to back in the spikelet. They open by a swelling of the lodicules which
force the lower flowering glumes through a right angle away from
the paleae, so that they stand vertically, one up and one down, with
the paleae horizontal between them. The stamens and stigmas of the
hermaphrodite flower emerge first, followed by the stamens of the
staminate flower. The long slender filaments suspend the anthers over
the sides of the paleae, where they sway in the slightest breeze, shedding
their pollen. The stigmas stand horizontally to left and right of the
paleae, well above the stamens. The pollen is very abundant and the
stigmas are large and feathery so that cross-pollination by wind readily
takes place, where, as is usual, the plants are crowded together.

The combination of an inconspicuous perianth, long flexible filaments,
abundant powdery pollen, and large feathery stigmas is very characteristic of wind-pollinated flowers. The presence of a single ovule in the
ovary is also very general in such flowers, though found also in many
insect-pollinated forms.

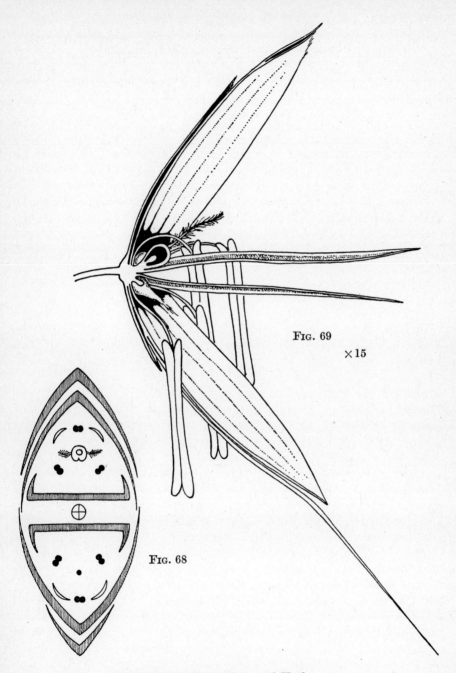

FIG. 69

×15

FIG. 68

Arrhenatherum elatius Mert. and Koch.

PLANTAGO MAJOR L.

PLANTAGINACEAE

GREAT PLANTAIN

Inflorescence: a slender racemose spike, 5–50 cm. long, elongating considerably in fruit, with closely-set flowers in the axils of ovate, fleshy, scarious-margined bracts.

Flower: hermaphrodite, actinomorphic.

CALYX: four diagonally-placed free sepals, ovate, green, with broad scarious margins.

COROLLA: actinomorphic, sympetalous; scarious, with short tube 1·5–2 mm., and four ovate-acute teeth, 1 mm., at first erect, later reflexed.

ANDROECIUM: four stamens, hypogynous or borne on the base of the corolla-tube, opposite the sepals; filaments colourless, long, slender, projecting from the corolla-tube; anthers reddish-purple or yellow, attached at the middle, drooping, with the pointed apex of the connective directed downwards; dehiscence by lateral slits.

GYNAECIUM: superior, syncarpous, bilocular, with four to six ovules per loculus on massive axile placentae; style unbranched, slender, hairy, projecting from the corolla-tube and stigmatic over the whole of the projecting part.

NECTARY: none.

Fruit: a capsule enclosed within the persistent bract, calyx, and corolla, and dehiscing transversely to release two to four seeds from each loculus.

Status: a native weed of waste land, flowering from May to September.

The Great Plantain has wind-pollinated flowers which are strongly protogynous, the long hairy stigmas protruding first while the anthers are still enclosed by the erect corolla-teeth, and beginning to wither soon after the anthers dehisce. In the second stage of flowering the corolla-teeth curve back and the slender filaments elongate, bending slightly under the weight of the anthers which are thus held out from the side of the spike. They swing about their point of attachment to the filament, and pollen is easily shaken out in the wind. The spike being racemose, flowers near the top may have only their stigmas protruding, while others lower down are in the staminate stage. Cross-pollination is favoured by protogyny, but there is a short period when pollen from dehiscing anthers may fall or be blown on to the stigma of the same flower.

The flowers are quite scentless and the filaments are slender, transparent, and colourless. In these features there is an interesting contrast with *Plantago media*, whose usually insect-pollinated flowers are scented and whose filaments are thicker and more rigid and bright purple in colour. There is a further conspicuous difference in the shape of the spike, long and slender in *P. major*, shorter and ovoid in *P. media*.

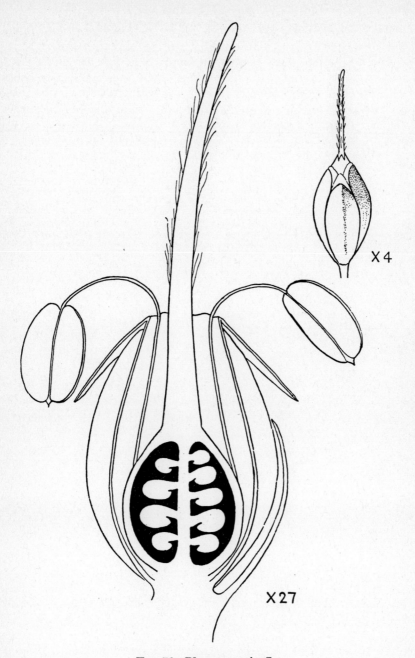

X 4

X 27

Fig. 70. *Plantago major* L.

PLANTAGO MEDIA L.

PLANTAGINACEAE

LESSER PLANTAIN

Inflorescence: a dense spike, 25–60 mm. long. Each flower is in the axil of a small green bract with transparent margins.

Flower: hermaphrodite, actinomorphic.

CALYX: four free sepals in a whorl. Each sepal is ovate, about 2 mm. long, and is green with a broad colourless scarious margin.

COROLLA: scarious, sympetalous with a tube 2 mm. long and four colourless, transparent, pointed teeth 1·5–2 mm. long, with margins slightly inrolled.

ANDROECIUM: four stamens borne on the base of the corolla-tube opposite the sepals; filaments reaching 6–9 mm. in length, slender, at first white but becoming pale purple; anthers white 2 mm. long, attached at the middle; connective ending in a small triangular flap; pollen grains small, round, and smooth.

GYNAECIUM: superior, syncarpous; ovary spherical, 0·7 mm. in diameter, bilocular, with two to three ovules on axile placentae in each loculus; style long and slender, reaching 7–10 mm. in length, pale purple, with long white stigmatic papillae over the whole of the part which projects from the corolla-tube.

NECTARY: none.

Fruit: a capsule surrounded by the persistent calyx, dehiscing transversely, so that its top comes off like a lid.

Status: a native perennial herb of short grassland, flowering in July and August.

The flowers are protogynous, the stigmas protruding before the corolla-teeth diverge. Later the corolla-teeth part slightly to allow the emergence of the bent filaments of the stamens. Later still the corolla-teeth diverge until they are horizontal, and the anthers are withdrawn by the straightening of the filaments. This takes place when the stigmas project for about 2 mm., but they continue to elongate during dehiscence of the anthers until they reach a length of 4–7 mm., and may remain receptive until after the stamens have withered. The filaments project from the corolla-tube for a distance of 6–9 mm. At first they make an angle of about 30° with the vertical, but later bend slightly downwards under the weight of the anthers. After dehiscence of the anthers they become irregularly twisted and bent with loss of turgor, and eventually wither.

A spike with most of its flowers in the staminate stage is made conspicuous by the purple filaments and white anthers, and is also sweetly scented. Short-tongued bees, pollen-eating flies, and beetles visit the flowers freely, and may effect cross-pollination of the upper flowers of a spike if they are still in the stigmatic stage or of the lower flowers whose anthers have withered. The incompleteness of the protogyny, however, makes self-pollination very probable while the anthers are dehiscing.

The long filaments though not as slender as those of Great Plantain, *Plantago major*, are nevertheless not rigid, and the anthers are attached in the middle, as in many wind-pollinated flowers. The pollen is only slightly adhesive, and there is little doubt that it is sometimes carried by wind to receptive stigmas. The flowers of Lesser Plantain seem, in fact, to stand on the border-line between entomophily and anemophily.

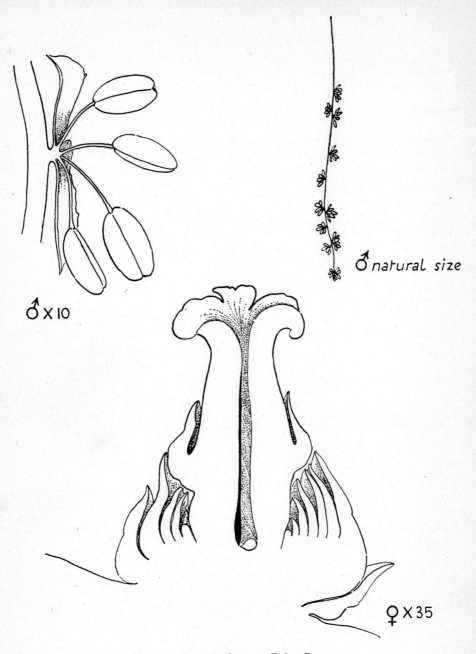

♂ × 10

♂ *natural size*

♀ × 35

FIG. 71. *Quercus Robur* L.

QUERCUS ROBUR L.

FAGACEAE

ENGLISH OAK

The trees are monoecious, with staminate and carpellary flowers in separate inflorescences.

Staminate Inflorescences: a slender pendulous spike or catkin, 50–100 mm. long, with about twelve flowers in the axils of small bracts, chiefly near the end of the axis. The catkins are borne in the axils of the uppermost bud-scales and lowest foliage leaves, so as to form tufts hanging from each expanding bud.

Staminate Flower:

PERIANTH: five to seven green segments, 1 mm. long.

ANDROECIUM: five to twelve stamens more or less opposite the perianth segments; filaments 1 mm. long; anthers small, 1 mm. long.

NECTARY: none.

Carpellary Inflorescence: an erect spike with two or three flowers in the axils of bracts near the end of the axis. Each flower has a basal cup of concrescent scales. The carpellary spikes are borne in the axils of foliage leaves in the upper part of the year's growth.

Carpellary Flower:

PERIANTH: six greenish scales, 0·5 mm. long, in two whorls of three.

GYNAECIUM: inferior, syncarpous; ovary becoming trilocular with two ovules per loculus on axile placentae; style short and thick; stigmas three, each two-lobed, with the lobes curved downwards.

NECTARY: none.

Fruit: an inferior nut, the acorn, with one or occasionally two seeds. The basal cup or 'cupule' of the carpellary flower grows with the ovary after fertilization and becomes the familiar 'acorn-cup' of the ripe fruit. In a strong wind the acorns may be blown a few yards from the parent tree, and they may occasionally be dropped accidentally by birds and small animals attempting to carry them away.

Status: the oak is a native tree forming woods on soils of widely different types. The flowers open at the end of May.

The carpellary flowers of Oak are pollinated by wind. The pollen is dry and powdery and is produced in considerable quantities from the pendulous catkins which sway readily in the wind. There is neither a brightly coloured corolla nor a scent to attract insects. Occasionally bees or flies collect pollen from the staminate flowers, but never visit the carpellary flowers and so cannot effect cross-pollination. Self-pollination is excluded by monoecism, but stigmas must very frequently receive pollen from staminate flowers of the same tree.

An interesting feature of the Oak, found also in Hazel, Hornbeam, Alder, and some other catkin-bearing trees, is that the ovaries of the carpellary flowers are still rudimentary at the time of pollination. This is the stage shown in the drawing. The partition-walls which ultimately make the ovary trilocular have not yet grown in from the side, and the ovules have not yet appeared. Pollination takes place in May, and while the pollen-tubes are growing down the stylar canal the ovary develops so that the ovules are ready for fertilization in late June or early July.

TABLE OF FLOWERS DESCRIBED AND
THEIR VISITORS

Species	Colour	Dichogamy	Nectar	Working Distance	Symmetry	Notes
A. Insect-Pollinated.						
1. Long-tongued Moths						
Lonicera Periclymenum L.	White	..	+	20–25 mm.	zyg.	Very fragrant: no landing stage: occasionally visited by long-tongued bees.
Melandrium album Garcke	White	dioec.	+	♀20–25 mm. ♂15–18 mm.	act.	Dioecious: opens only at night: fragrant.
2. Humble-Bees						
Aconitum Napellus L.	Blue-purple	protand.	+++	10–15 mm.	zyg.	Short-tongued bees perforate the spurs.
Aquilegia vulgaris L.	Blue-purple	protand.	+++	10–17 mm.	act.	
Delphinium (hybrid)	Blue-purple,etc.	protand.	+++	13–20 mm.	zyg.	Smaller insects may rob nectar without pollinating.
Digitalis purpurea L.	Red-purple	protand.	+	..	zyg.	Short-tongued humble-bees perforate the corolla.
Lamium album L.	White	..	+	10 mm.	zyg.	
Lupinus polyphyllus Lindl.	Blue-purple,etc.	protand.	−	..	zyg.	Hive-bees not heavy enough to depress keel.
3. Various Bees						
Geranium pratense L.	Blue-purple	protand.	++	1–2 mm.	act.	Hive-bees.
Helleborus niger L.	White	protog.	++	2–3 mm.	act.	Hive-bees and Anthophora pilipes: often selfed.
Lathyrus odoratus L.	Red-purple	protand.	++	15 mm.	zyg.	Cultivated varieties usually selfed.
Primula vulgaris Huds.	Yellow	..	++	10–20 mm.	act.	Dimorphic: chief visitor Anthophora pilipes.
Sarothamnus scoparius Wimm.	Yellow	protand.	−	..	zyg.	Explosive: small bees, flies, and beetles take pollen after explosion.
Scilla nutans Sm.	Blue-purple	protog.	++	..	act.	Pendulous: chiefly hive-bees.
Viola odorata L.	Blue-purple	..	++	6–8 mm.	zyg.	Hive-bees reach nectar only with difficulty: chief visitor Anthophora pilipes.

	Colour		Nectar	Length	Symmetry	Remarks
4. Bees and long-tongued Flies						
Centaurea Cyanus L.	Blue-purple	protand.	+	5–6 mm.	(act.)	Also visited by butterflies.
Chrysanthemum carinatum L.	White and red	protand.	+	2–5 mm.	(act.)	Sometimes self-sterile.
Ranunculus acris L.	Yellow	..	+	1–2 mm.	act.	
Rubus Idaeus L.	Greenish-white	..	+	4–6 mm.	act.	
Taraxacum officinale L.	Yellow	protand.	+	3–7 mm.	(act.)	
(Caltha palustris L.)	Yellow	..	+	2–4 mm.	act.	Nectar secreted in damp air).
5. Bees and pollen-seeking Flies						
Caltha palustris L.	Yellow	..	+	2–4 mm.	act.	Visited chiefly for pollen.
Clematis vitalba L.	Greenish-white	..	+	..	act.	Slight nectar-secretion from filaments.
Plantago media L.	Purple	protog.	–	..	act.	Conspicuous colour due to filaments of stamens.
Thalictrum aquilegifolium L.	Purple	protog.	–	..	act.	
6. Wasps						
Scrophularia aquatica L.	Red-brown	protog.	+	2–4 mm.	zyg.	
7. Nectar-seeking Flies						
Heracleum Sphondylium L.	White	protand.	..	..	act.	Much visited also by beetles.
Arum maculatum L.	Green and red-brown	monoec. (protog.)	..	..	act.	Chiefly visited by tiny midges (Psychodidae).
B. Wind-Pollinated						
Arrhenatherum elatius Mert. and Koch.	Green	..	–	..	zyg.	
Plantago major L.	Green	protog.	–	..	act.	
Quercus Robur L.	Green	monoec.	–	..	act.	
Thalictrum minus L.	Green	..	–	..	act.	

zyg. = zygomorphic; act. = actinomorphic: + = nectar secreted; – = no nectar; protand. = protandrous; protog. = protogynous; monoec. = monoecious; dioec. = dioecious.

GLOSSARY

Achene: a dry one-seeded indehiscent fruit: p. 33.

Actinomorphic: radially symmetrical (of a flower): p. 5.

Androecium: collective name for all the stamens of a flower: p. 5.

Anemophilous: pollinated by wind: p. 22.

Apocarpous: consisting of separate carpels (cp. Syncarpous): p. 8.

Asymmetrical: having no plane of symmetry (of a flower): p. 5.

Axil: the angle immediately above the point of insertion of a lateral organ, especially of a leaf.

Axis: a stem or shoot: floral axis—that part of a shoot which bears the floral organs; the receptacle: p. 3.

Berry: a one- or more-seeded fruit whose wall is succulent throughout: p. 34.

Bract: the more or less reduced leaves, in whose axils inflorescences, partial inflorescences, or flowers are borne: p. 1.

Bracteole: the tiny leaves, usually two in Dicotyledons and one in Monocotyledons, borne on the flower-stalk. In a branched inflorescence the bracteoles of one flower may function as bracts of others: p. 3.

Calyx: a collective term for all the sepals of a flower: p. 4.

Capitulum: an inflorescence of numerous closely packed unstalked flowers on a flat or rounded receptacle; a head: p. 2.

Capsule: a dry dehiscent fruit formed from a syncarpous ovary; p. 32. *See also* Siliqua *and* Silicula.

Carpellary: having a functional ovary but no functional stamens (of a unisexual flower): p. 11.

Catkin: an inflorescence in which unstalked or very shortly stalked flowers are borne on an axis which hangs down from the parent axis; a pendulous spike.

Chitin: the material of which the hard exterior of most insects is formed.

Claw: the basal part of a petal, if it resembles a flattened stalk (cp. limb).

Cleistogamous: self-pollinated without opening: p. 25.

Concrescent: involved in a common zone of growth so as to form a single structure.

Connective: that part of the filament of a stamen to which the anther lobes are attached: p. 5.

Corolla: collective term for all the petals of a flower: p. 4.

Corona: corolla-like structure within the true corolla, consisting of outgrowths from the petals or from the stamens. The 'trumpet' of a daffodil is a very large corona: p. 43.

Corymb: an inflorescence either racemose or cymose in which the flower-stalks arise at different heights on the main axis but their lengths are so adjusted that the flowers are borne at the same level: p. 2.

Cupule: a cup-like structure partially or completely enclosing one or more ovaries: p. 107.

Cyme: an inflorescence in which each axis terminates in a flower, and branching is confined to the axils of bracts close beneath the terminal flower: p. 1.

    Helicoid cyme: a cyme in which each axis branches once, and always on the same side: p. 1.

    Scorpioid cyme: a cyme in which each axis branches once, but alternately to the left and to the right: p. 1.

Dehiscence: the splitting open of a pollen sac, fruit, &c.: pp. 6, 32.

Dichasium: a cymose inflorescence in which each axis has two lateral branches, usually borne at the same level: p. 1.

Dichogamy: a difference in time of maturation of anthers and stigmas; includes Protandry and Protogyny: p. 20.

Dioecious: having unisexual flowers, the staminate and carpellary flowers being borne on different individual plants: p. 11.

Drupe: a one- or more-seeded fruit the outer part of whose wall is succulent while the inner part is hard, forming one or more 'stones' enclosing the seeds: p. 34.

Drupelet: a small drupe, usually one of many as in a Blackberry or Raspberry: p. 85.

Entomophilous: pollinated by insects.

Epigynous: upon the ovary: describes the mode of insertion of the floral members in a flower with an inferior ovary and is also used more loosely of the whole flower when the ovary is inferior: p. 9.

False fruit: a fruit to which other structures than the ovary contribute: p. 34.

Floral diagram: a conventional representation of the ground plan of a flower: p. 39.

Follicle: a dry fruit derived from a single carpel and dehiscing only along its inner side: p. 32.

Gamosepalous: consisting of sepals carried up on a common zone of growth so as to form a basal tube: p. 5.

Glandular: bearing glands or secretory cells.

Glume: the chaffy scales which replace bracts and bracteoles in grasses and sedges: p. 101.

Gynaecium: a collective term for the ovaries of a flower with their styles and stigmas: p. 7.

Hermaphrodite: having both functional stamens and functional ovaries (of a flower): p. 10.

Hydrophilous: pollinated by water: p. 24.

Hypogynous: below the ovary: describes the mode of insertion of the other floral members in certain flowers with a superior ovary, and is also used more loosely of the whole flower having this mode of insertion: p. 8.

Inferior: Inferior ovary: p. 9.
Inferior fruit: one derived from an inferior ovary: p. 33.

Intercalary growth: growth, localized or diffuse, in a region other than at the apex of an organ: p. 9.

Involucre: a collective term for a number of bracts which are borne close together to form a protective often calyx-like structure beneath an inflorescence or flower: an involucre is especially characteristic of the family *Compositae*: p. 87.

Lanceolate: long and narrow, and broadest at or below the middle.

Legume: a dry fruit formed from a single carpel, and dehiscing both along the inside and outside; a pod; especially characteristic of the family *Leguminosae*: p. 32.

Limb: the expanded, blade-like part of a petal which has a claw.

Loculus: a chamber, especially of an ovary or fruit; hence unilocular, bilocular, trilocular: having one, two, three loculi: p. 8.

Lodicule: the tiny scales, usually two in number, found at the front of the flower in grasses, and believed to be vestigial perianth segments: p. 101.

Meristem: a region of actively dividing cells.

Monochasium: a cymose inflorescence each axis of which has a single lateral branch: scorpioid and helicoid cymes (see Cyme) are special types of monochasia: p. 1.

Monoecious: having unisexual flowers, with both kinds borne on the same individual plant: p. 10.

Nectary: the glandular tissue which secretes the sugary solution called nectar; also the organ on which this tissue is found: p. 15.

Nut: a one-seeded dry indehiscent fruit whose wall is very hard: p. 33.

Ovate: having an egg-shaped outline, broadest below the middle.

Panicle: a branched racemose inflorescence; the branches may be either racemose or cymose: p. 1.

Papilla: a small rounded projection; used especially of the irregularly projecting cells of the stigma, which are usually sticky through the secretion of a sugary solution.

Pappus: a collective term for the simple or branched hairs which replace the calyx in the florets of many *Compositae*, and which form a tuft above the ripe fruit: p. 87.

Perianth: a collective term for the outermost floral organs (excluding bracteoles) when these are not differentiated into sepals and petals: p. 4.

Perigynous: round the ovary: describes the mode of insertion of the other floral members in certain flowers with a superior ovary, and is also more loosely used of the whole flower having this mode of insertion: p. 9.

Placenta: an area of attachment of ovules to the inside of the ovary wall: p. 8. Hence placentation: mode of attachment of ovules.

Polygamous: having unisexual and hermaphrodite flowers: p. 11.

Pome: a special kind of succulent fruit formed from the inferior ovary of the apple and its allies: p. 34.

Primordium: a part of a plant or plant organ in the earliest stages of its development when it consists of cells which are still dividing and has not yet acquired its characteristic form.

Receptacle: the floral axis, whose variation in forms give rise to the terms hypogynous, perigynous, epigynous: p. 3; also used of the much expanded end of the inflorescence-axis of the capitulum of the *Compositae*.

Scarious: membranous, like parchment.

Siliqua, Silicula: special kinds of capsule found in *Cruciferae*, and other allied families: p. 33.

Spathe: a large bract or bracteole which encloses an inflorescence or flower in bud and may remain conspicuous when the flower has opened: p. 4.

Spikelet: a small spike; especially the compact partial inflorescence of a grass or sedge. In grasses the spikelet consists typically of an axis bearing near its base two empty glumes, and then a varying number of flowering glumes each with a flower in its axil.

Spur: a tapering tube, closed at the end, formed from one or more floral members; petal spurs often hold nectar secreted from their walls or elsewhere and their position determines the way in which insects behave on reaching the flower: p. 16.

Staminate: having functional anthers but no functional ovaries (of a unisexual flower): p. 11.

Staminode: a stamen, or a structure in the place of a stamen, which does not form functional pollen: p. 11.

Sympetalous: consisting of petals carried up on a common zone of growth so as to form a basal tube: p. 5.

Syncarpous: the product of a common zone of growth beneath a number of carpel primordia so that a single structure is formed (of an ovary): p. 8.

Triad: a group of three flowers; a dichasial triad consists of a terminal flower with two younger lateral flowers beneath it, thus giving a very simple cymose inflorescence: p. 41.

Umbel: an inflorescence in which all the flower stalks arise from the same level at the end of the parent axis; a compound umbel branches once or more often, the branches arising in a whorl at the end of the parent axis: p. 2.

Whorl: a set of lateral members which arise at the same level on the parent axis; used especially of floral parts, which generally arise in this manner: p. 3.

Zygomorphic: having only one plane of symmetry (of a flower): p. 5.

SELECTED BIBLIOGRAPHY

CHURCH, A. H. *Types of Floral Mechanism.* Oxford, 1908.
> Established a standard for the description and drawing of flowers.

DARWIN, C. *The Fertilization of Orchids.* London, 1862.
> Describes in detail the pollination mechanism of a number of orchids: excellent figures.

DARWIN, C. *The Effects of Cross and Self Fertilization in the Vegetable Kingdom.* London, 1876.
> An account of experiments demonstrating hybrid vigour.

EAST, E. M., and JONES, D. F. *Inbreeding and Outbreeding.* Philadelphia, 1919.
> Considers cross- and self-fertilization from standpoint of modern genetics.

EICHLER, A. W. *Blüthendiagramme.* Leipzig, 1875.
> Describes the arrangement of parts in representative flowers from all families and gives numerous floral diagrams.

KNUTH, P. *Handbook of Flower Pollination.* Translated by J. R. Ainsworth Davis. Oxford, 1906.
> Based on Müller's Book: an encyclopaedia of pollination mechanisms and insect visitors.

MÜLLER, H. *The Fertilization of Flowers.* Translated and edited by D'Arcy W. Thompson. London, 1883.
> The classic of flower-pollination.

PAYER, J.-B. *Traité d'Organogénie Comparée de la Fleur.* Paris, 1857.
> Series of very beautiful steel engravings showing stages in the development of numerous flowers, with full descriptions.

SKENE, MACGREGOR. *The Biology of Flowering Plants.* London, 1924.
> Has a valuable chapter on Reproduction and Dispersal including an account of recent experimental work on colour vision and sense of smell in insects.

PRINTED IN GREAT BRITAIN AT THE UNIVERSITY PRESS, OXFORD
BY JOHN JOHNSON, PRINTER TO THE UNIVERSITY

7 140